Grade 1

Play and Talk Korean

This book belongs to:

____

Note for Learners and Educators

In this book, we've adapted the Romanization of some Korean sounds to aid English speakers with pronunciation.

For example, '이' is officially Romanized as "i" but is represented here as "yee" to match its spoken sound in Korean more closely. This phonetic adaptation will be more accessible and intuitive for beginners.

Keep in mind that while these adaptations can help with pronunciation, they differ from the standard Romanization used in formal Korean language learning resources.

Paperback ISBN: 978-1-998277-21-6

Table of Contents

Korean syllables have two main parts: a consonant and a vowel. Some of these words also have '받침 [bat-chim],' a final consonant at the bottom, but not all words have it. Look at the word below and read it out loud.

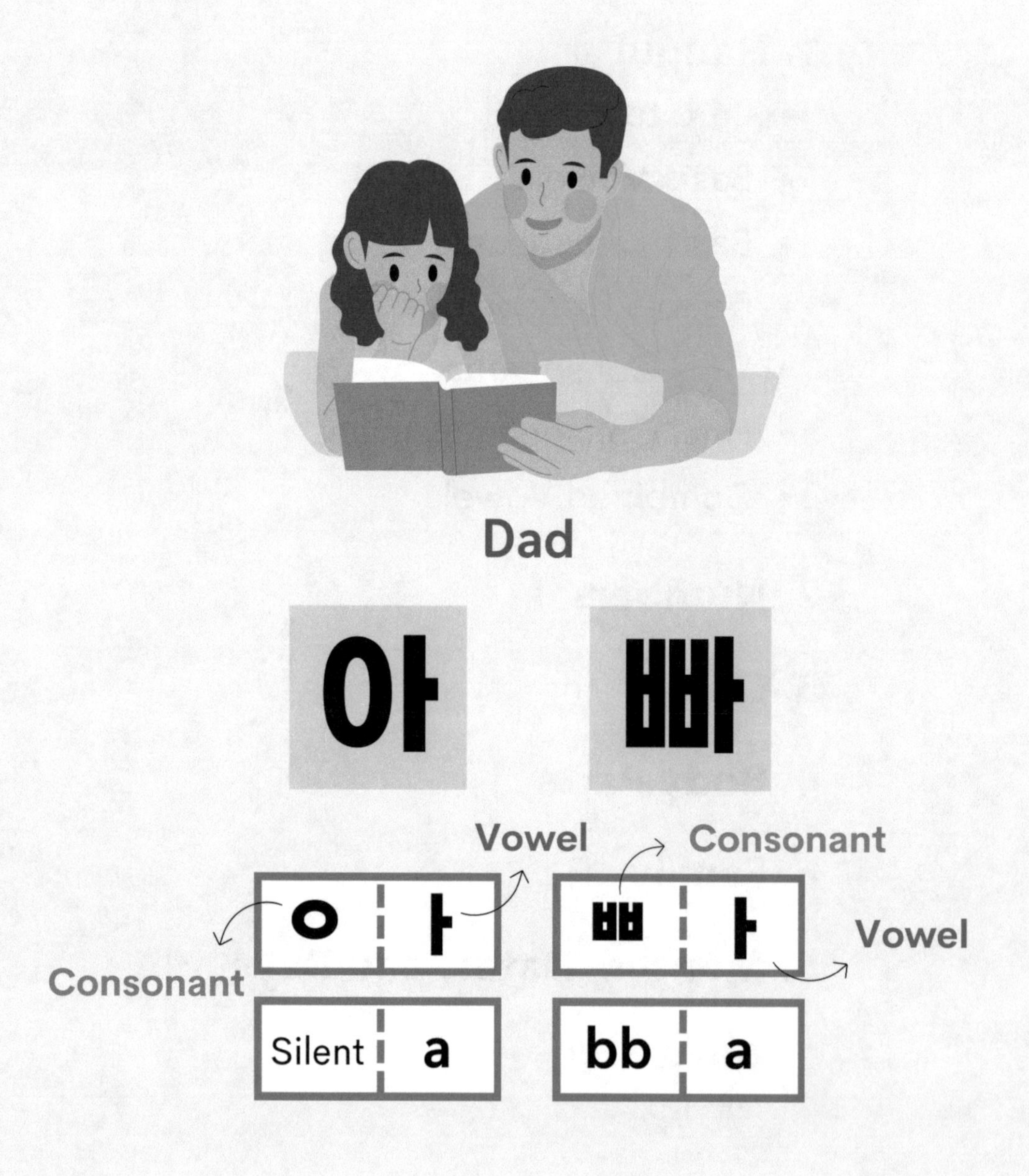

Example: Syllable with a final consonant, 받침 [bat-chim]

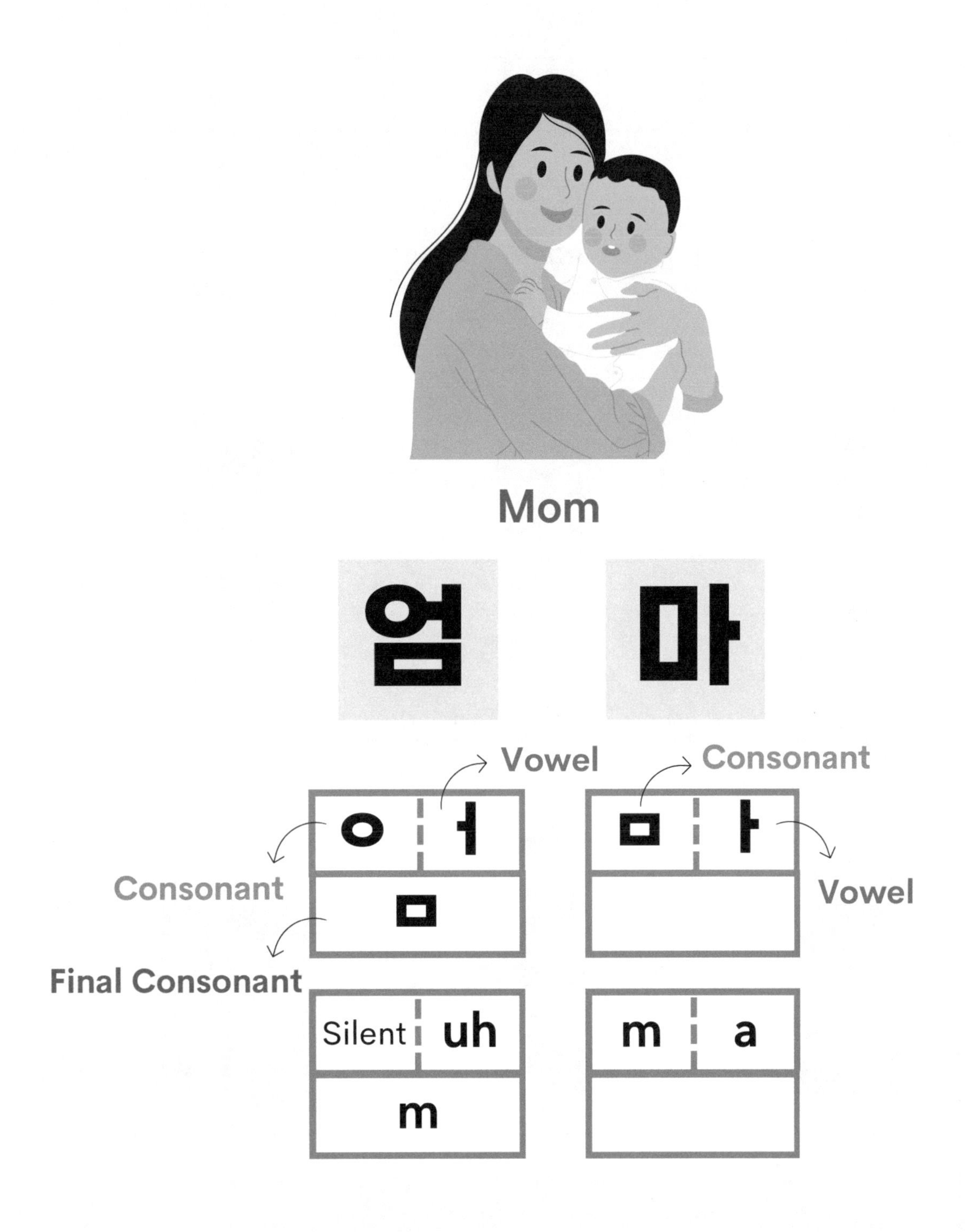

Date: / /

Basic vowel: ㅏ [a]/[ah]

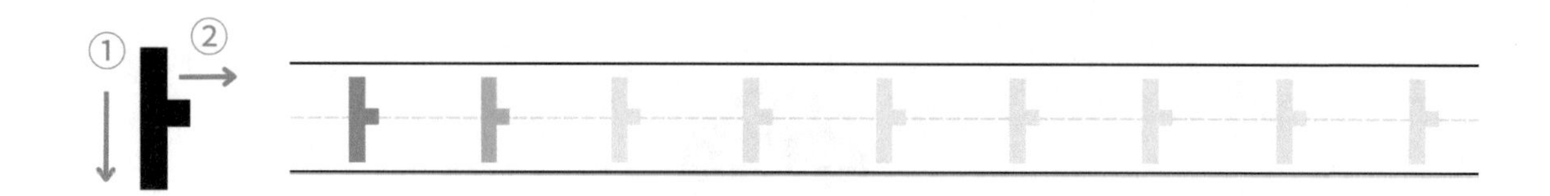

Find the vowel, 'ㅏ' [a]/[ah], and circle them all. The first one is the example.

Tree

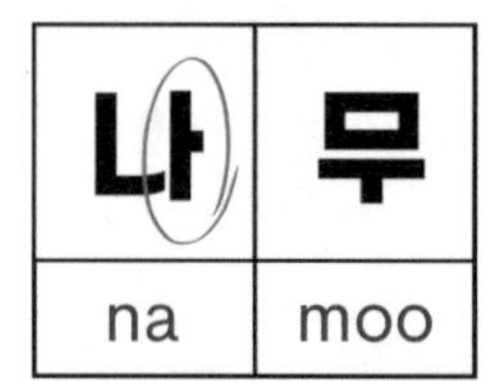

나	무
na	moo

Lion

사	자
sa	ja

Dad

아	빠
a	bba

Bag

가	방
ga	bang

Leg

다	리
da	lee

Train

기	차
gi	cha

Basic vowel: ㅑ [ya]

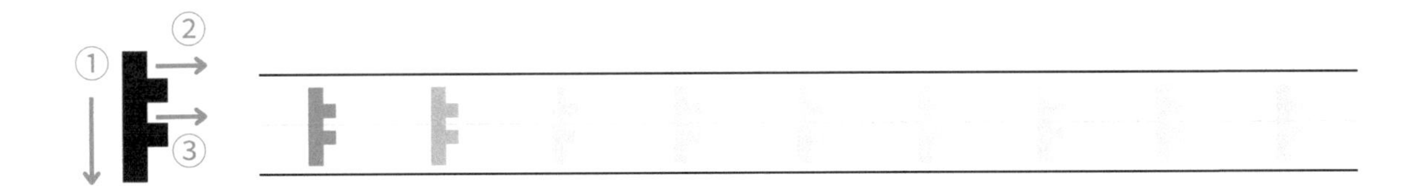

Find the vowel, ' ㅑ ' [ya], and circle them all.

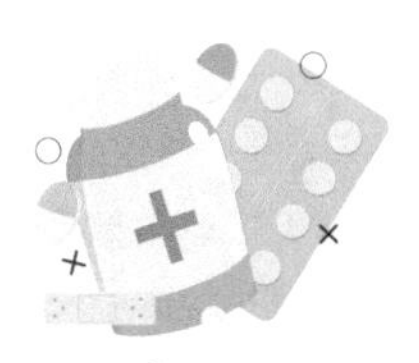

Medicine

약
yak

Baseball

야	구
ya	goo

Socks

양	말
yang	mal

Story

이	야	기
yee	ya	gi

Sheep

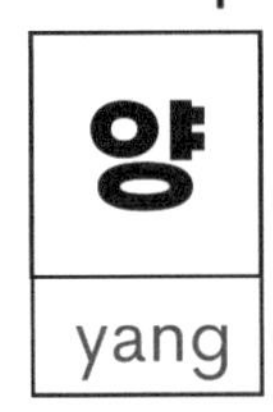

양
yang

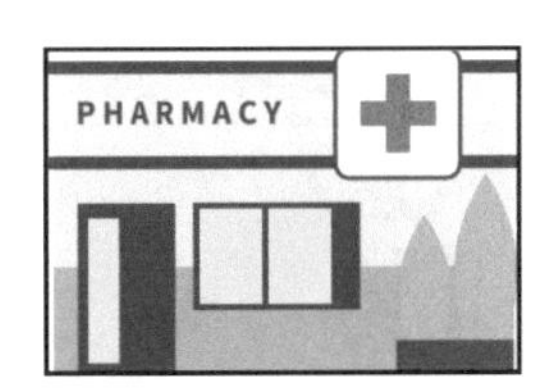

Pharmacy

약	국
yak	gook

Basic vowel: ㅓ [uh] *Sounds like [ʌ] as in "bug"

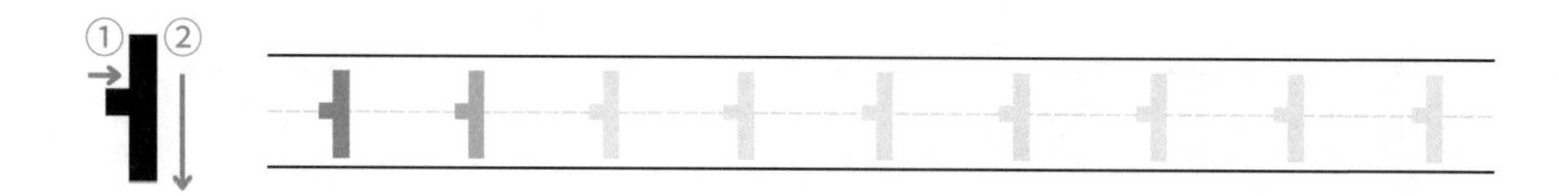

Find the vowel, 'ㅓ' [uh], and circle them all.

Mom

엄	마
uhm	ma

Spider

거	미
guh	mee

Present

선	물
suhn	mool

Mole

두	더	지
doo	duh	ji

Earphones

이	어	폰
yee	uh	pon

Kid/Child

어	린	이
uh	lin	yee

Basic vowel: ㅕ [yuh] * Commonly written as [yeo]

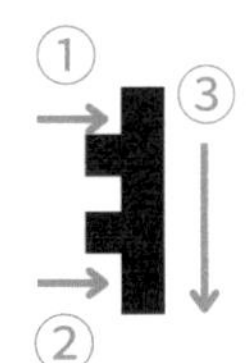

Find the vowel, ' ㅕ ' [yuh], and circle them all.

Fox

여	우
yuh	woo

English Language

영	어
yeong	uh

Winter

겨	울
gyuh	wool

Shuttle

셔	틀	버	스
shuh	teul	buh	seu

Woman

여	자
yuh	ja

Six

여	섯
yuh	suht

Date: /   /

Basic vowel: ㅗ [o]/[oh]

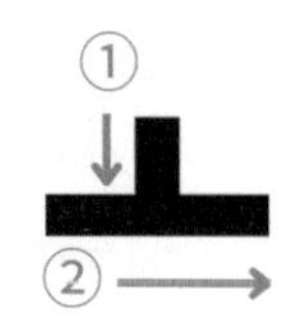

Find the vowel, 'ㅗ' [o]/[oh], and circle them all.

Cucumber

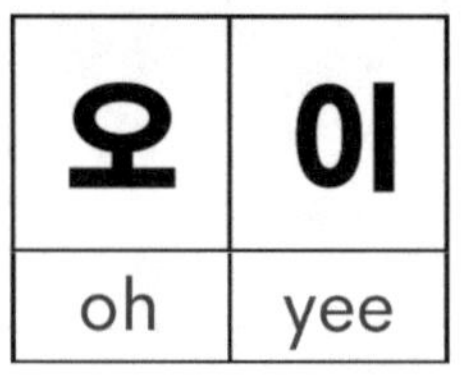

오	이
oh	yee

Hat

모	자
mo	ja

Cat

고	양	이
go	yang	yee

Rabbit / Bunny

토	끼
to	kkee

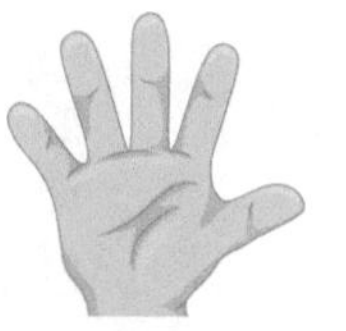

Hand

손
sohn

Meat

고	기
go	gi

Basic vowel: ㅛ [yo]

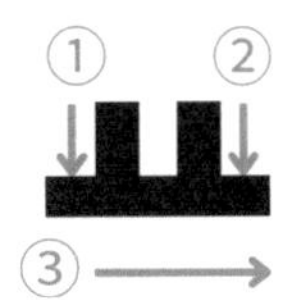

Find the vowel, 'ㅛ' [yo], and circle them all.

Cooking

요	리
yo	lee

Yogurt

요	거	트
yo	guh	teu

Classroom

교	실
gyo	shil

Yacht

요	트
yo	teu

Dragon

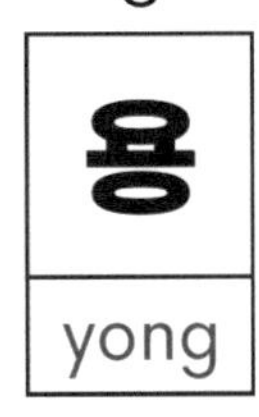

용
yong

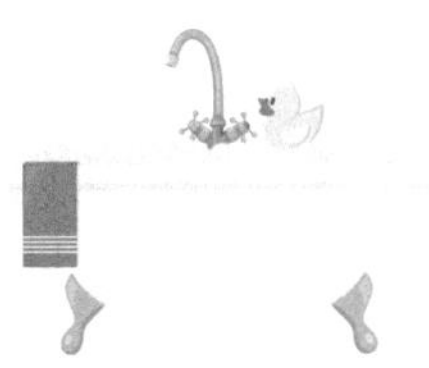

Bathtub

욕	조
yok	jo

Basic vowel: ㅜ [woo]

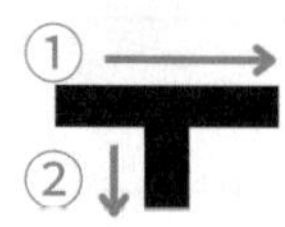

Find the vowel, 'ㅜ' [woo], and circle them all.

Umbrella

우	산
woo	san

Watermelon

수	박
soo	bak

Soap

비	누
bee	noo

Soccer/Football

축	구
chook	goo

Walnut

호	두
ho	doo

(Leather) Shoes

구	두
goo	doo

Basic vowel: ㅠ [yu]

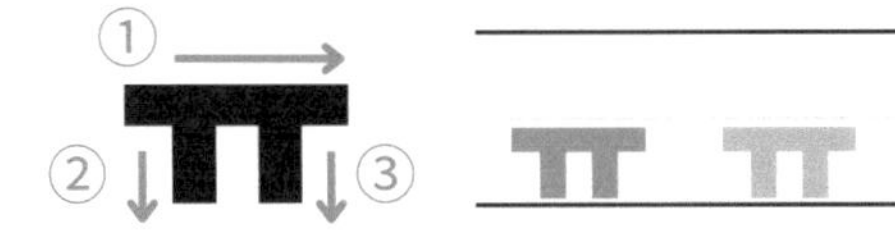

Find the vowel, 'ㅠ' [yu], and circle them all.

Milk

우	유
woo	yu

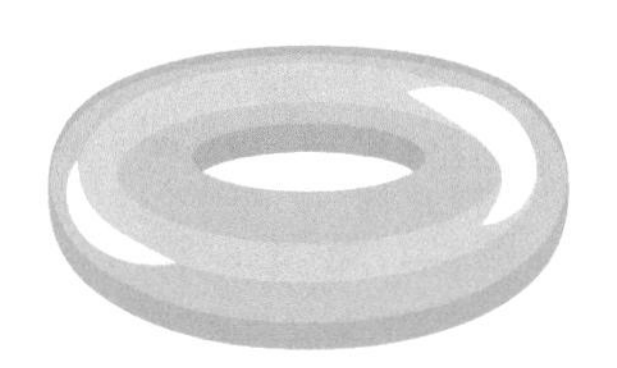

Floatie

튜	브
tyu	beu

Germ

세	균
se	gyun

Toilet paper

휴	지
hyu	jee

Freedom

자	유
ja	yu

Tangerine

귤
gyul

Date: / /

Basic vowel: ㅡ [eu]

Find the vowel, 'ㅡ' [eu], and circle them all.

Swing

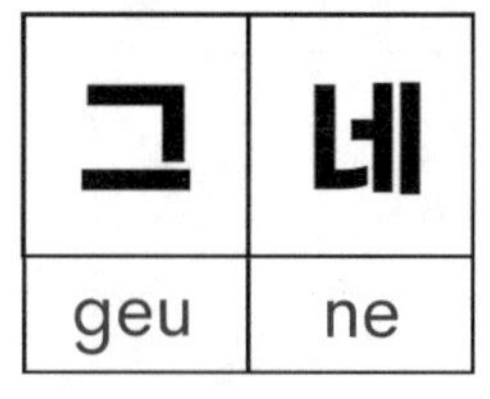

그	네
geu	ne

Bus

버	스
buh	seu

Broccoli

브	로	콜	리
beu	loh	kol	lee

Deer

사	슴
sa	seum

Shadow

그	림	자
geu	lim	ja

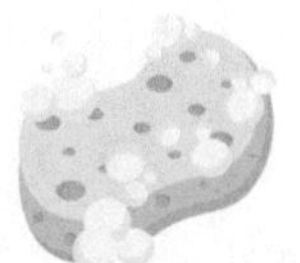

Sponge

스	펀	지
seu	puhn	jee

Basic vowel: ㅣ [yee]

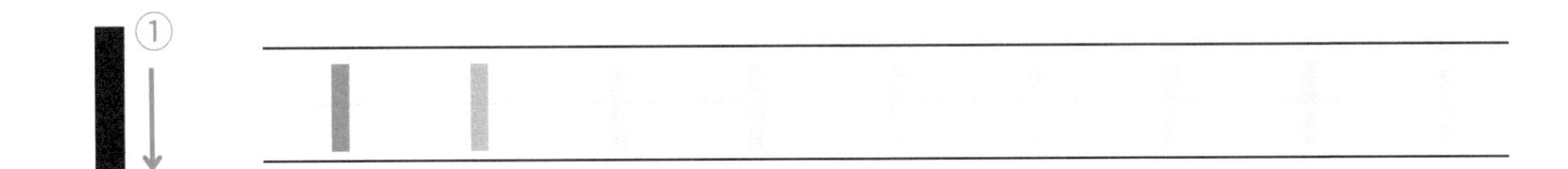

Find the vowel, ' ㅣ ' [yee], and circle them all.

Pizza

피	자
pee	ja

Toothpaste

치	약
chee	yak

Headband

머	리	띠
muh	lee	ttee

Strawberry

딸	기
ttal	gi

Airplane

비	행	기
bee	hang	gi

Seesaw

시	소
shee	so

Finding the correct vowels

uh ㅏ ㅑ ㅓ ㅕ ㅗ ㅛ ㅜ ㅠ ㅡ ㅣ

yo ㅏ ㅑ ㅓ ㅕ ㅗ ㅛ ㅜ ㅠ ㅡ ㅣ

eu ㅏ ㅑ ㅓ ㅕ ㅗ ㅛ ㅜ ㅠ ㅡ ㅣ

yuh ㅏ ㅑ ㅓ ㅕ ㅗ ㅛ ㅜ ㅠ ㅡ ㅣ

oh ㅏ ㅑ ㅓ ㅕ ㅗ ㅛ ㅜ ㅠ ㅡ ㅣ

woo ㅏ ㅑ ㅓ ㅕ ㅗ ㅛ ㅜ ㅠ ㅡ ㅣ

ah ㅏ ㅑ ㅓ ㅕ ㅗ ㅛ ㅜ ㅠ ㅡ ㅣ

yah ㅏ ㅑ ㅓ ㅕ ㅗ ㅛ ㅜ ㅠ ㅡ ㅣ

yee ㅏ ㅑ ㅓ ㅕ ㅗ ㅛ ㅜ ㅠ ㅡ ㅣ

yu ㅏ ㅑ ㅓ ㅕ ㅗ ㅛ ㅜ ㅠ ㅡ ㅣ

Matching vowels

Draw a line to match the vowel on the left to its pronunciation letter on the right.

ㅜ •	• yee
ㅑ •	• uh
ㅗ •	• ah
ㅣ •	• yu
ㅠ •	• ya
ㅡ •	• oh
ㅕ •	• yuh
ㅏ •	• yo
ㅛ •	• eu
ㅓ •	• woo

Date: / /

Basic consonant: ㄱ 기역 [gi yeok]

The first consonant, 'ㄱ' (기역 [gi yeok]), is pronounced like [g] at the beginning of words or syllables. Trace and write 'ㄱ'.

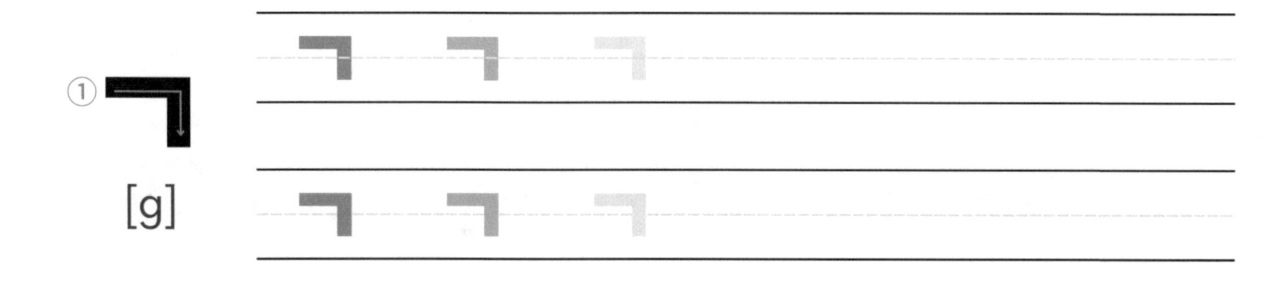

Combine 'ㄱ' (기역 [gi yeok]) with the basic vowels. Trace, write, and read them out loud.

	[ah]	[ya]	[uh]	[yuh]	[oh]	[yo]	[woo]	[yu]	[eu]	[yee]
+	ㅏ	ㅑ	ㅓ	ㅕ	ㅗ	ㅛ	ㅜ	ㅠ	ㅡ	ㅣ
ㄱ	가	갸	거	겨	고	교	구	규	그	기
[g]	[ga]	[gya]	[guh]	[gyuh]	[go]	[gyo]	[goo]	[gyu]	[geu]	[gi]

가 갸 거 겨 고 교 구 규 그 기

가 갸 거 겨 고 교 구 규 그 기

■ Choose the correct word from the word bank below for each picture, and write it to complete the words.

	차
gi	cha

	기
go	gi

	방
ga	bang

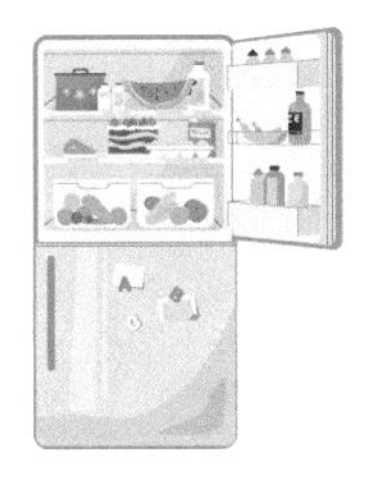

냉	장	
neng	jang	go

햄	버	
ham	buh	guh

이	야	
yee	ya	gi

가방 (Bag) 기차 (Train) 이야기 (Story)

햄버거 (Hamburger) 고기 (Meat) 냉장고 (Refrigerator)

Basic consonant: ㄴ 니은 [nee eun]

The 'ㄴ' (니은 [nee eun]) is pronounced like [n] at the beginning of words or syllables. Trace and write 'ㄴ'.

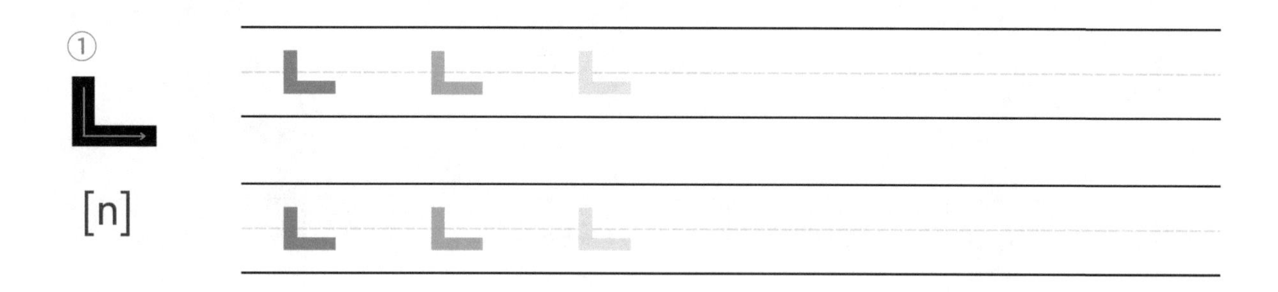

Combine 'ㄴ' (니은 [nee eun]) with the basic vowels. Trace, write, and read them out loud.

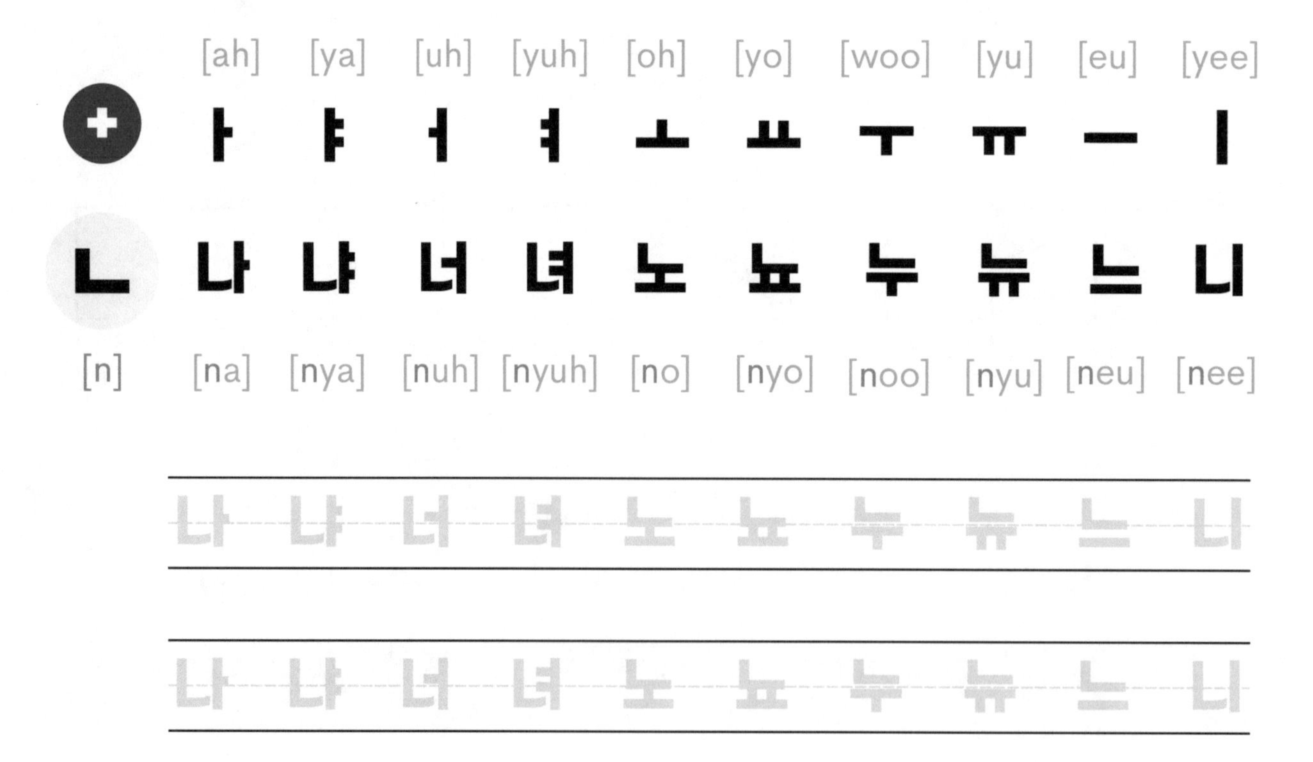

■ Choose the correct word from the word bank below for each picture, and write it to complete the words.

바		
ba	na	na

피	아	
pee	ah	no

	쵸
na	cho

	구	리
nuh	goo	lee

도	
do	nut

	사	람
noon	sa	lam

나쵸 (Nacho) 바나나 (Banana) 눈사람 (Snowman)

도넛 (Doughnut) 너구리 (Raccoon) 피아노 (Piano)

Date: / /

Basic consonant: ㄷ 디귿 [dee geut]

The 'ㄷ' (디귿 [dee geut]) is pronounced like [d] at the beginning of words or syllables. Trace and write 'ㄷ'.

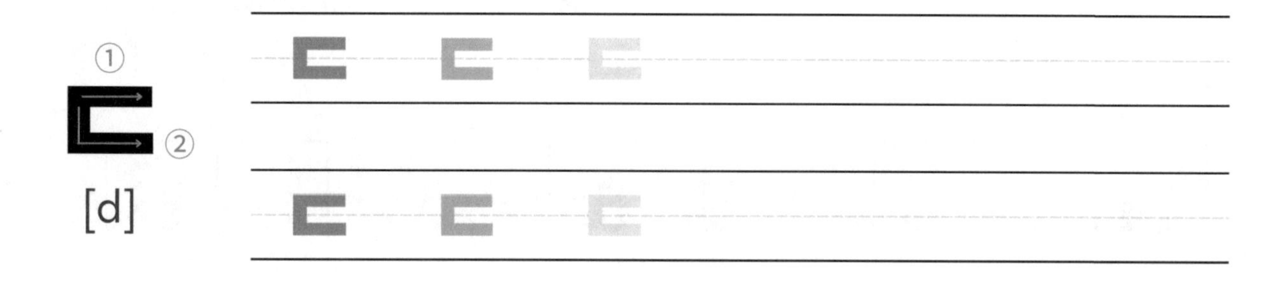

Combine 'ㄷ' (디귿 [dee geut]) with the basic vowels. Trace, write, and read them out loud.

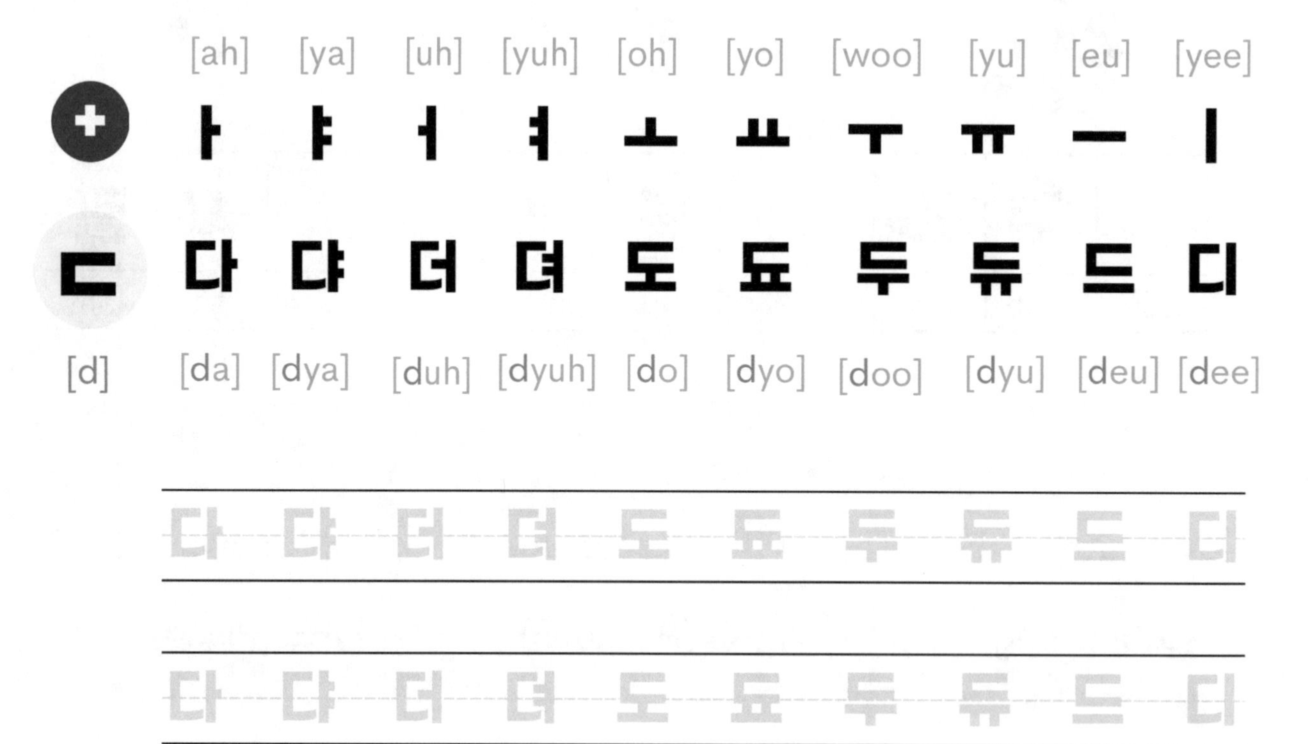

■ Choose the correct word from the word bank below for each picture, and write it to complete the words.

	리
da	lee

샐	러	
sael	luh	deu

	부
doo	boo

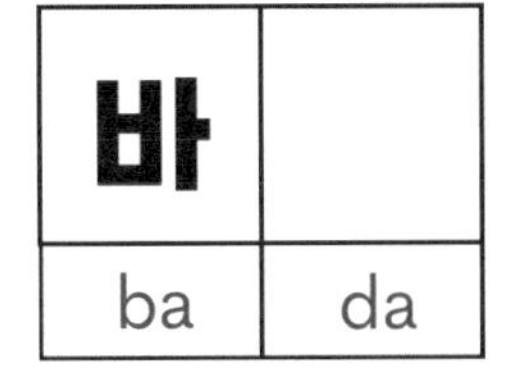

바	
ba	da

사		리
sa	da	lee

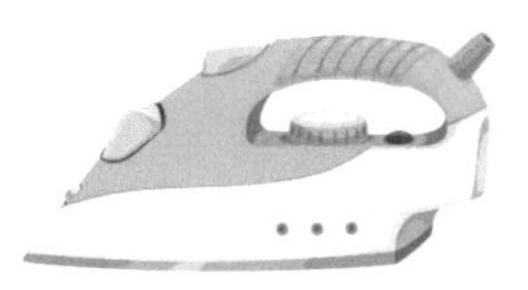

	리	미
da	lee	mee

사다리 (Ladder) 두부 (Tofu) 다리 (Bridge)

바다 (Sea/Ocean) 다리미 (Iron) 샐러드 (Salad)

Basic consonant: ㄹ 리을 [lee eul]

The 'ㄹ' (리을 [lee eul]) is pronounced like the blends of [l] or [r] depending on its position in a word and the vowels that follow it.

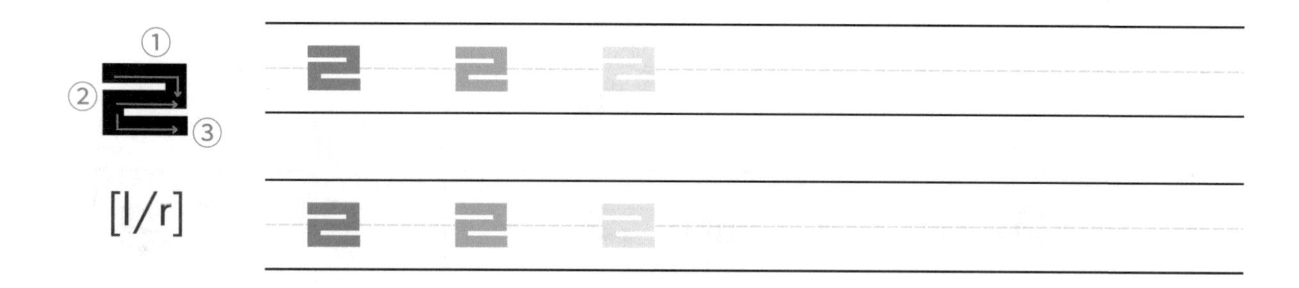

Combine 'ㄹ' (리을 [lee eul]) with the basic vowels. Trace, write, and read them out loud.

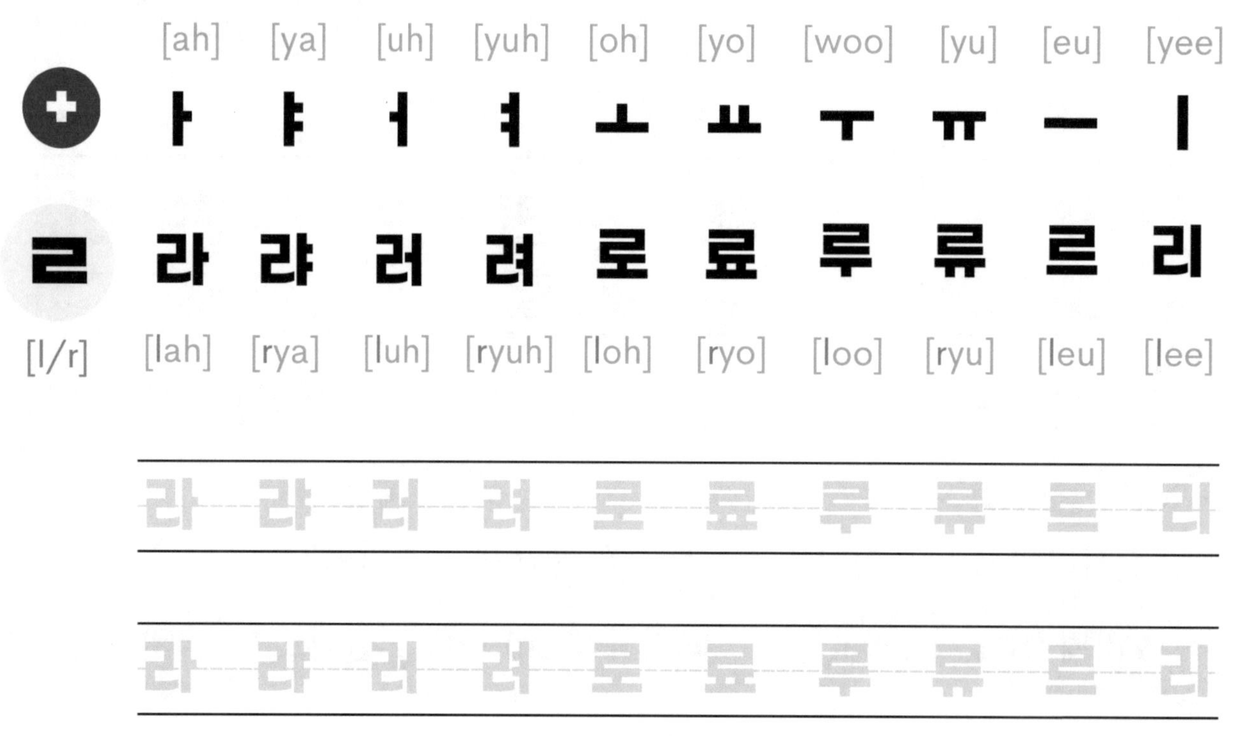

■ Choose the correct word from the word bank below for each picture, and write it to complete the words.

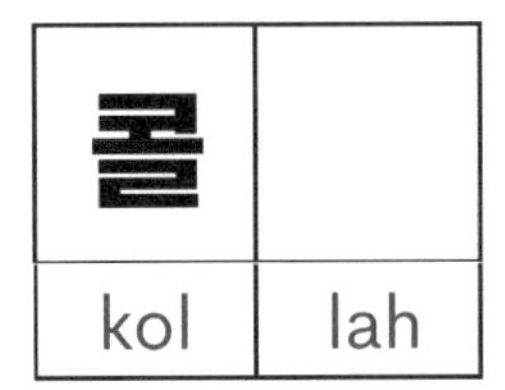

콜	
kol	lah

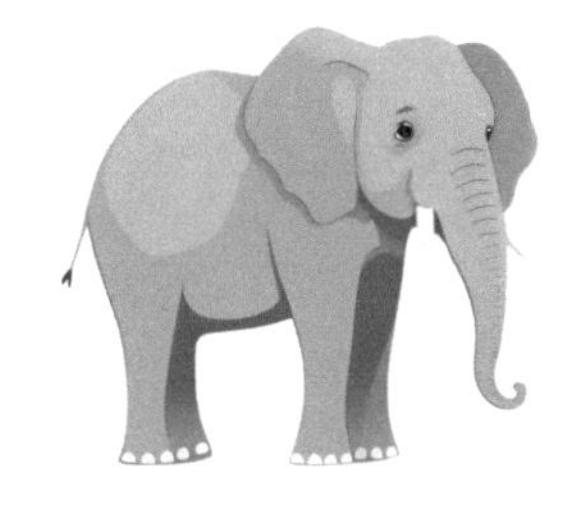

코	끼	
ko	kki	lee

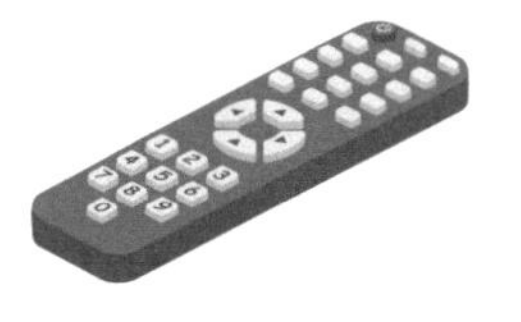

	모	컨
lee	mo	kuhn

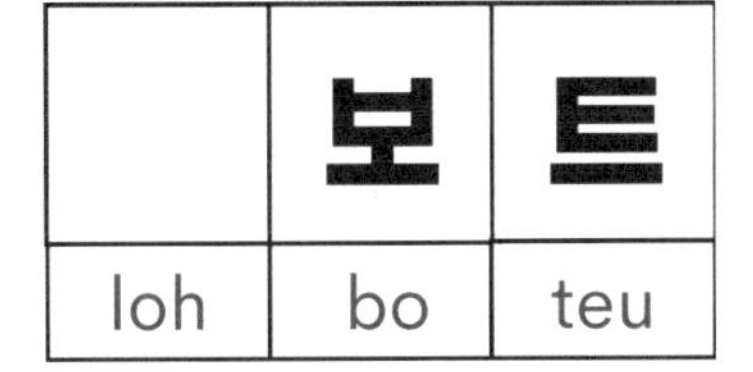

	보	트
loh	bo	teu

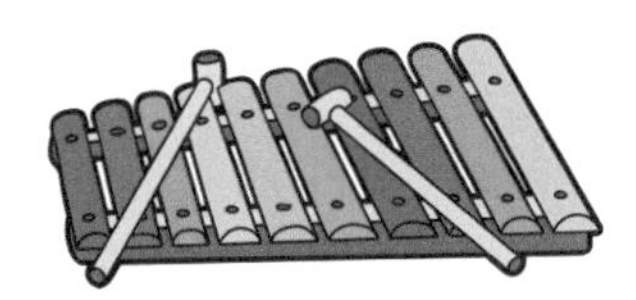

실		폰
shil	loh	pon

	면
lah	myeon

실로폰 (Xylophone)　　로보트 (Robot)　　코끼리 (Elephant)

리모컨 (Remote controller)　　콜라 (Cola)　　라면 (Rameyon)

Date: / /

Basic consonant: ㅁ 미음 [mee eum]

The 'ㅁ' (미음 [mee eum]) is pronounced like [m] at the beginning of words or syllables. Trace and write 'ㅁ'.

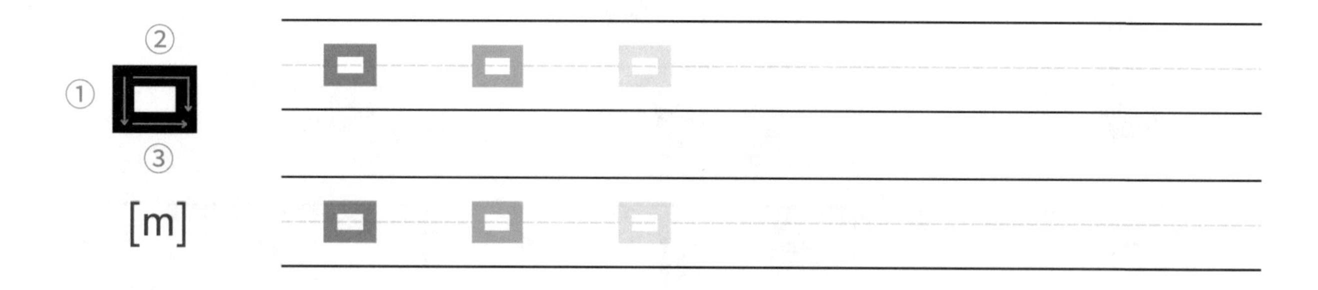

Combine 'ㅁ' (미음 [mee eum]) with the basic vowels. Trace, write, and read them out loud.

■ Choose the correct word from the word bank below for each picture, and write it to complete the words.

할머니 (Grandma)	마늘 (Garlic)	이마 (Forehead)
모기 (Mosquito)	미국 (USA)	모래 (Sand)

Basic consonant: ㅂ 비읍 [bee eup]

The 'ㅂ' (비읍 [bee eup]) is pronounced like [b] at the beginning of words or syllables. Trace and write 'ㅂ'.

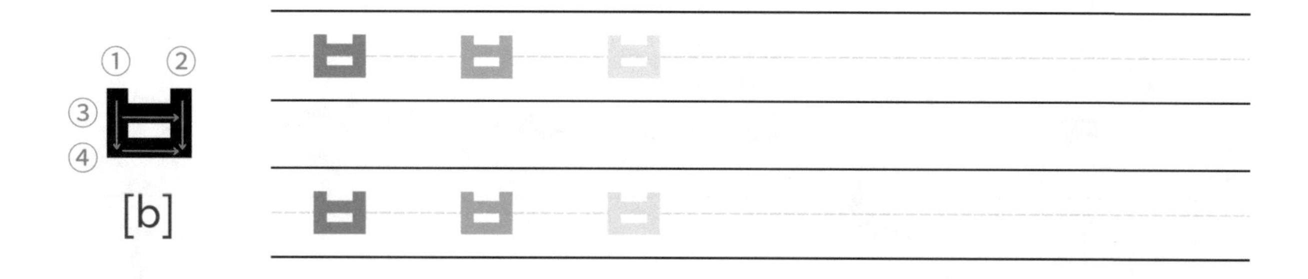

Combine 'ㅂ' (비읍 [bee eup]) with the basic vowels. Trace, write, and read them out loud.

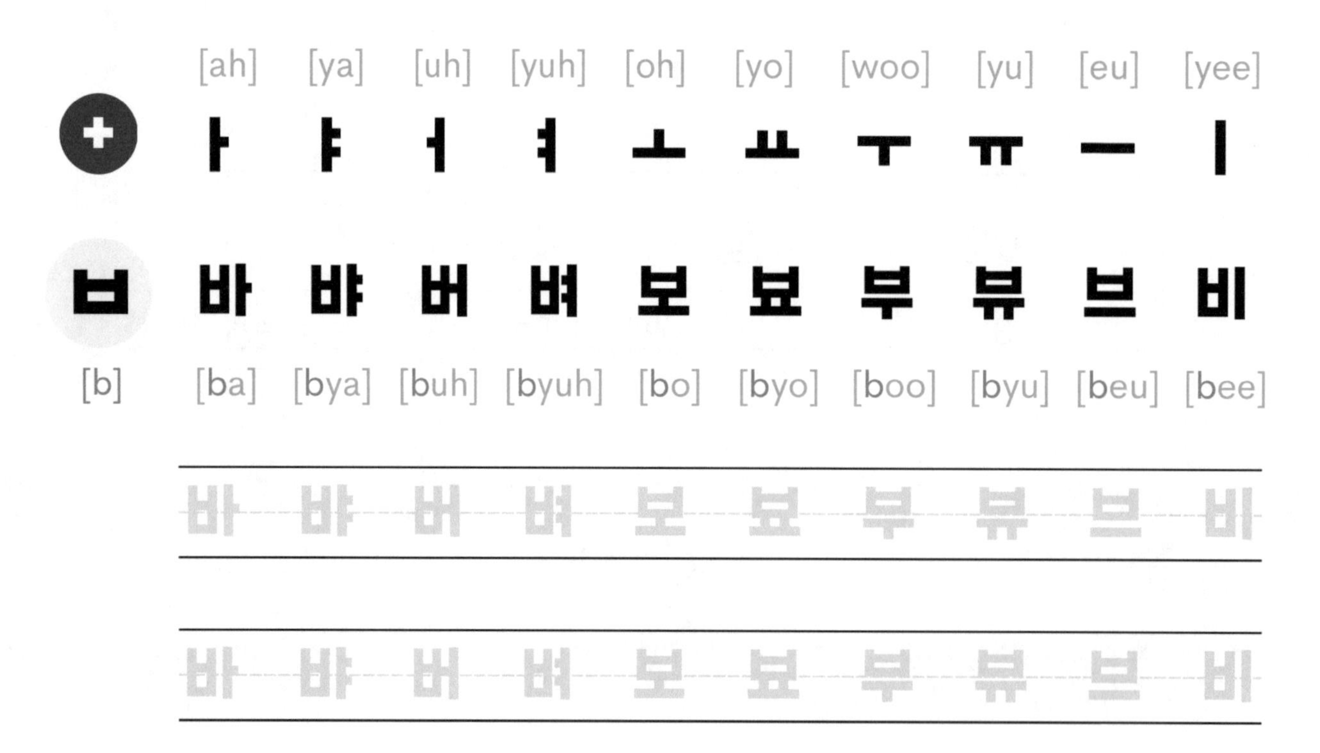

■ Choose the correct word from the word bank below for each picture, and write it to complete the words.

비누 (Soap) 공부 (Study) 비 (Rain)

비닐백 (Plastic Bag) 바지 (Pants) 비빔밥 (Bee Bim Bap)

Date: / /

Basic consonant: ㅅ 시옷 [shi oht]

The 'ㅅ' (시옷 [shi oht]) is pronounced like the blends of [s] or [sh] depending on its position in a word and the vowels that follow it.

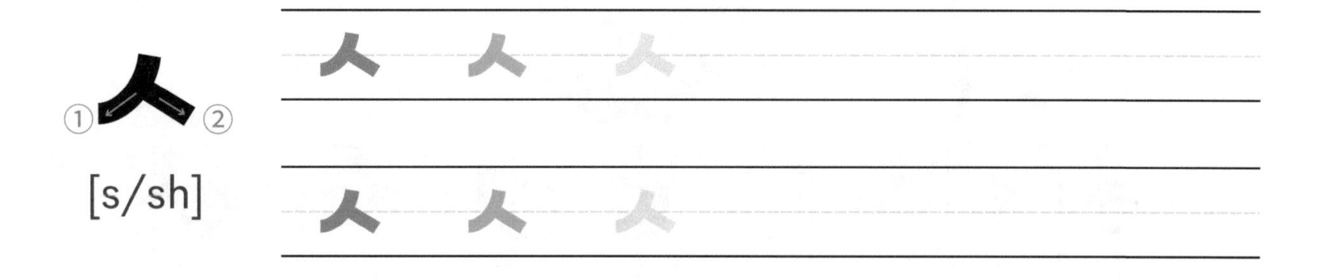

Combine 'ㅅ' (시옷 [shi oht]) with the basic vowels. Trace, write, and read them out loud.

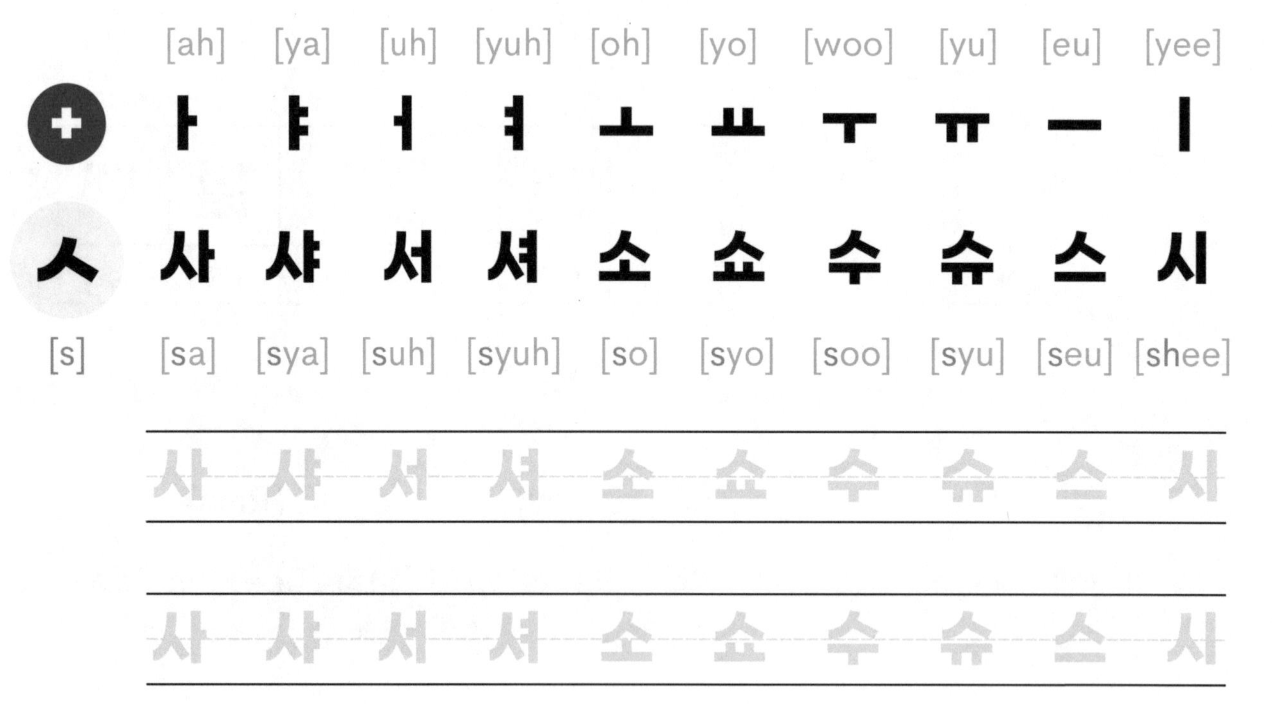

■ Choose the correct word from the word bank below for each picture, and write it to complete the words.

사진 (Photo) 서울 (Seoul) 사탕 (Candy)

소시지 (Sausage) 세수 (To wash face) 시소 (Seesaw)

Basic consonant: ㅇ 이응 [yee eung]

The 'ㅇ' (이응 [yee eung]) is silent when it precedes a vowel at the beginning of a syllable and is pronounced like [ng] when it's used as a final consonant (받침 [bat-chim]).

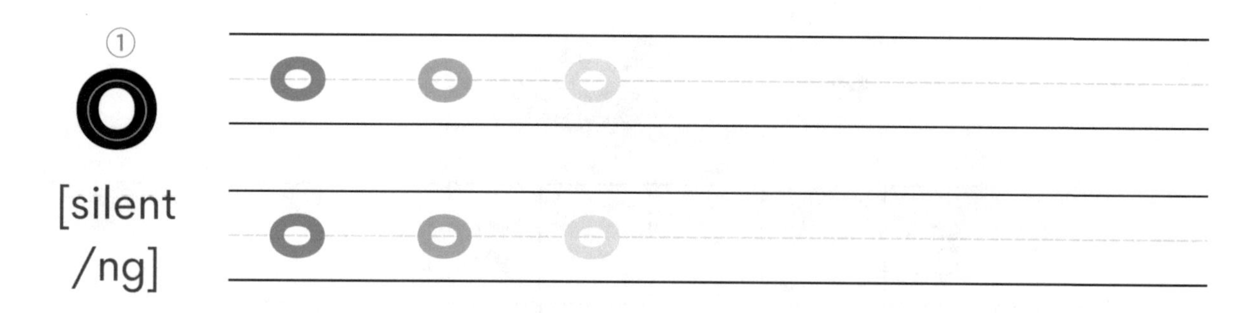

Combine 'ㅇ' (이응 [yee eung]) with the basic vowels. Trace, write, and read them out loud.

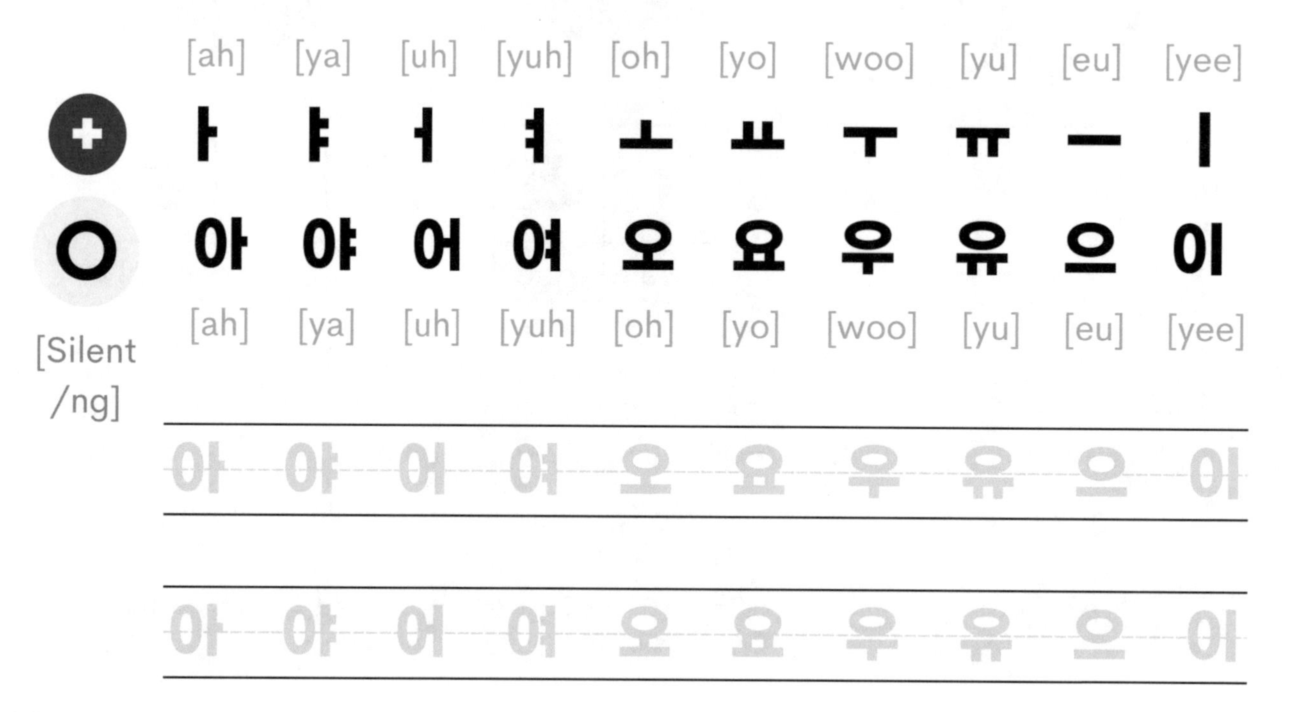

■ Choose the correct word from the word bank below for each picture, and write it to complete the words.

		스	크	림
ah	yee	seu	keu	lim

	징	
oh	jing	uh

상	
sang	uh

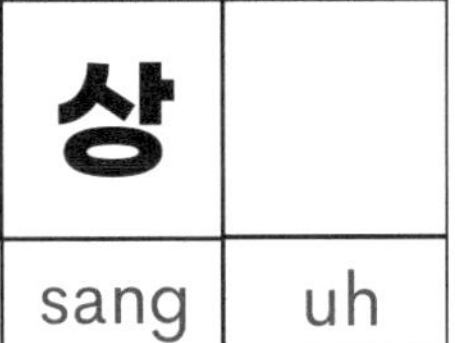

yuh	woo

	기
ah	gi

오징어 (Squid)　　아기 (Baby)　　상어 (Shark)

여우 (Fox)　　아이스크림 (Ice Cream)

Date: / /

Basic consonant: ㅈ 지읒 [jee eut]

The 'ㅈ' (지읒 [jee eut]) is pronounced similar to [j] at the beginning of words or syllables. Trace and write 'ㅈ'.

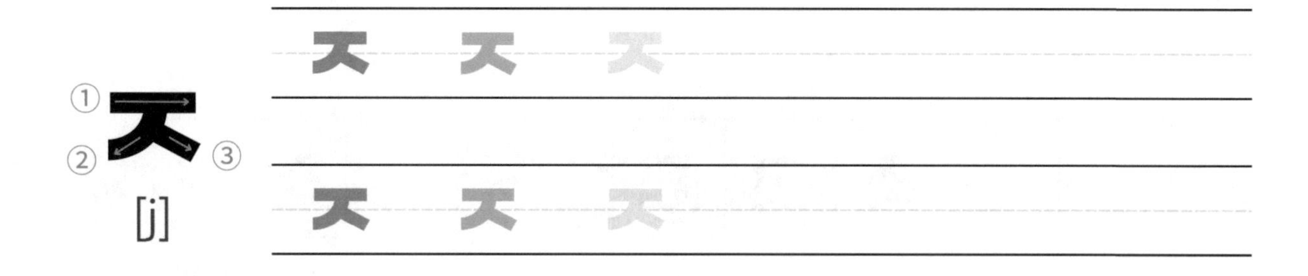

Combine 'ㅈ' (지읒 [jee eut]) with the basic vowels. Trace, write, and read them out loud.

	[ah]	[ya]	[uh]	[yuh]	[oh]	[yo]	[woo]	[yu]	[eu]	[yee]
+	ㅏ	ㅑ	ㅓ	ㅕ	ㅗ	ㅛ	ㅜ	ㅠ	ㅡ	ㅣ
ㅈ	자	쟈	저	져	조	죠	주	쥬	즈	지
[j]	[ja]	[jya]	[juh]	[jyuh]	[jo]	[jyo]	[joo]	[jyu]	[jeu]	[jee]

자 쟈 저 져 조 죠 주 쥬 즈 지

자 쟈 저 져 조 죠 주 쥬 즈 지

■ Choose the correct word from the word bank below for each picture, and write it to complete the words.

	전	거
ja	juhn	guh

휴	
hyu	jee

	말
joo	mal

	개
jo	gae

	붕
jee	boong

	동	차
ja	dong	cha

주말 (Weekend) 자동차 (Car) 휴지 (Toilet paper)

지붕 (Roof) 자전거 (Bicycle) 조개 (Clam)

Basic consonant: ㅊ 치읓 [jee eut]

The 'ㅊ' (치읓 [chee eut]) is pronounced similar to [ch] at the beginning of syllables and can sound closer to [t] when it serves as a final consonant (받침 [bat-chim]) in a word.

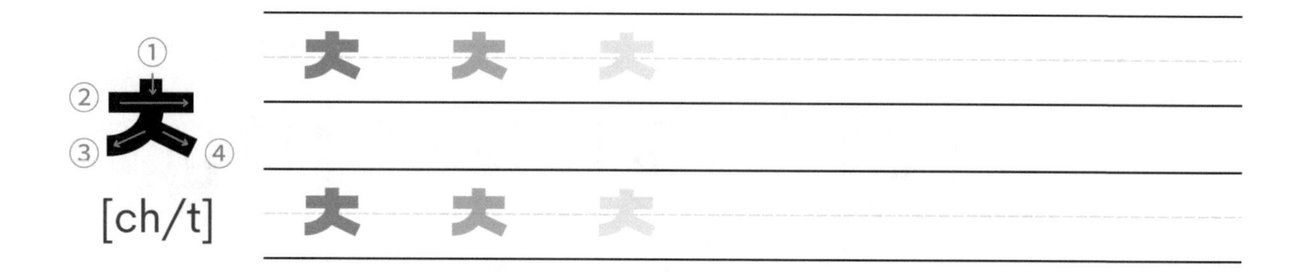

Combine 'ㅊ' (치읓 [chee eut]) with the basic vowels. Trace, write, and read them out loud.

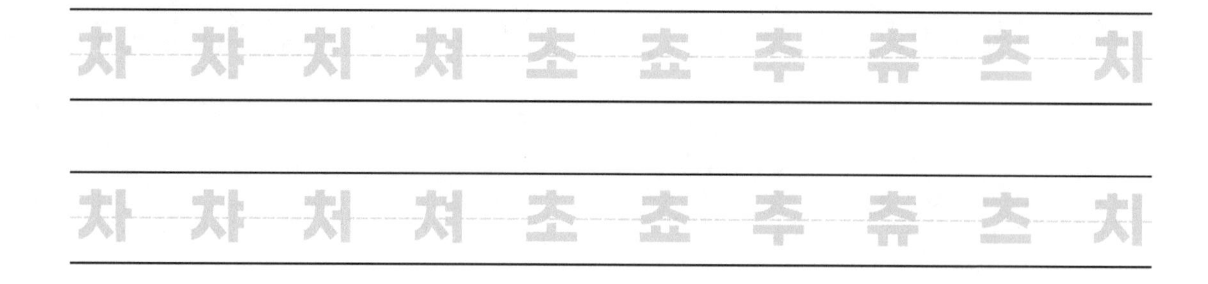

■ Choose the correct word from the word bank below for each picture, and write it to complete the words.

기	
gi	cha

유		원
yu	chee	won

	타
chee	ta

티	셔	
tee	shuh	cheu

식	
shik	cho

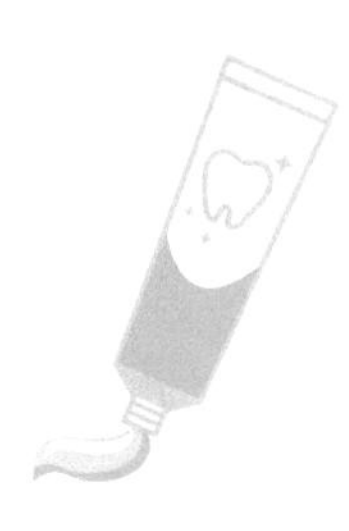

	약
chee	yak

식초 (Vinegar) 치약 (Toothpaste) 티셔츠 (T-shirt)

유치원 (Kindergarten) 치타 (Cheetah) 기차 (Train)

Date: / /

Basic consonant: ㅋ 키읔 [kee euk]

The 'ㅋ' (키읔 [kee euk]) is pronounced similar to a hard [k], as in 'kite,' at the beginning of words or syllables. Trace and write 'ㅋ'.

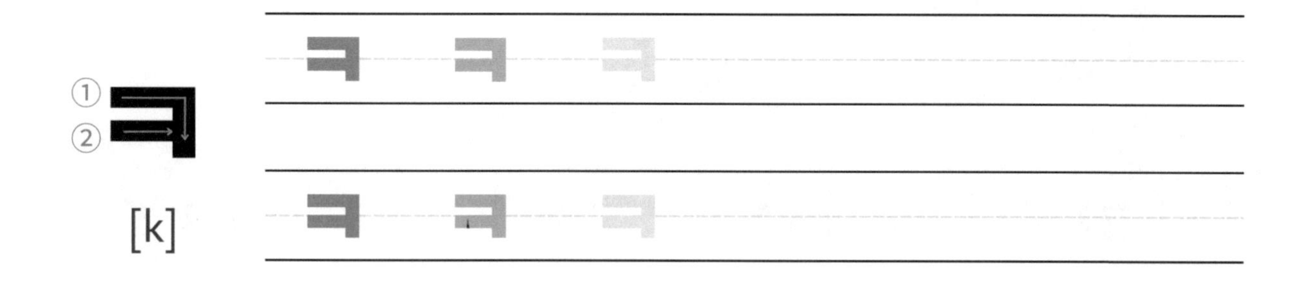

Combine 'ㅋ' (키읔 [kee euk]) with the basic vowels. Trace, write, and read them out loud.

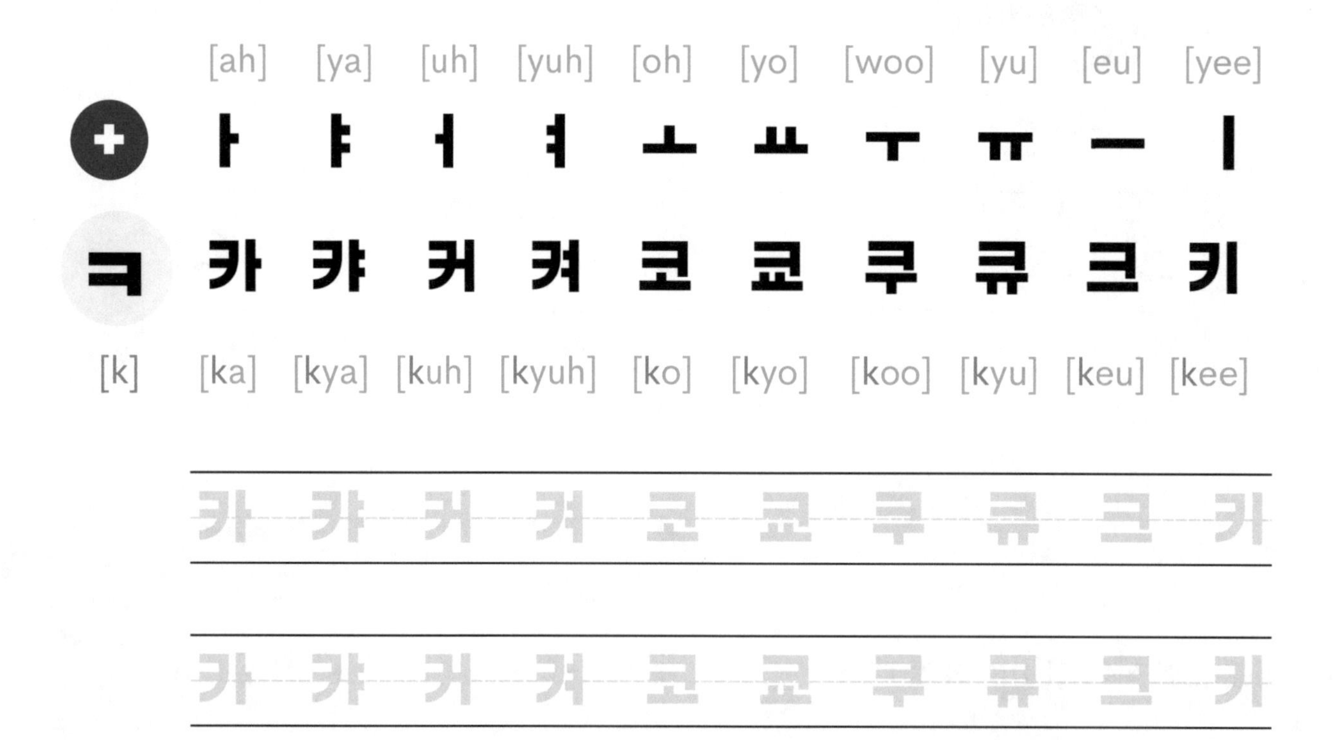

■ Choose the correct word from the word bank below for each picture, and write it to complete the words.

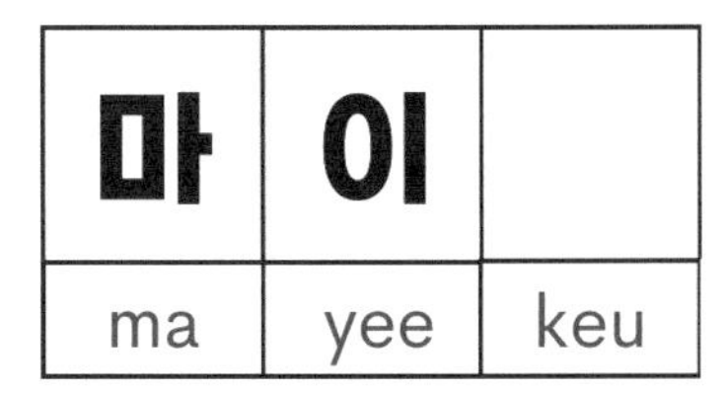

마	이	
ma	yee	keu

koo	kee

	메	라
ka	meh	la

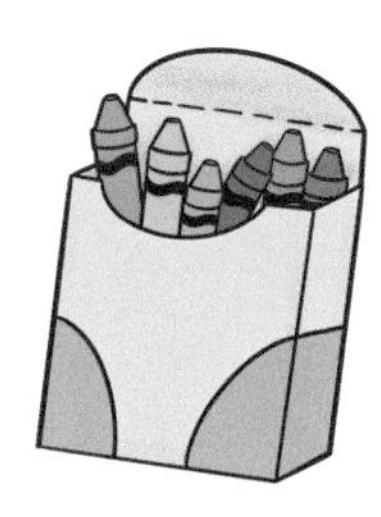

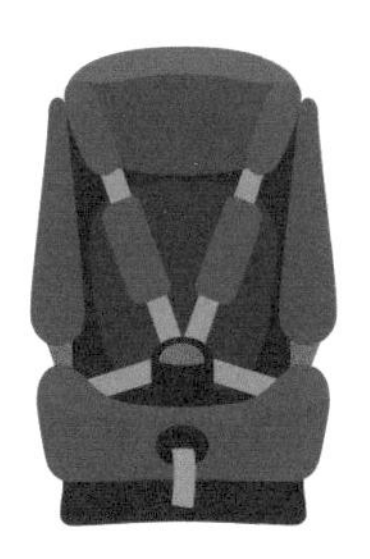

	레	용
kue	leh	yong

	피
kuh	pee

	시	트
ka	shee	teu

쿠키 (Cookie)   커피 (Coffee)   마이크 (Microphone)

카시트 (Car Seat)   크레용 (Crayon)   카메라 (Camera)

Basic consonant: ㅌ 티읕 [tee eut]

The 'ㅌ' (티읕 [tee eut]) is pronounced like [t] at the beginning of words or syllables. Trace and write 'ㅌ'.

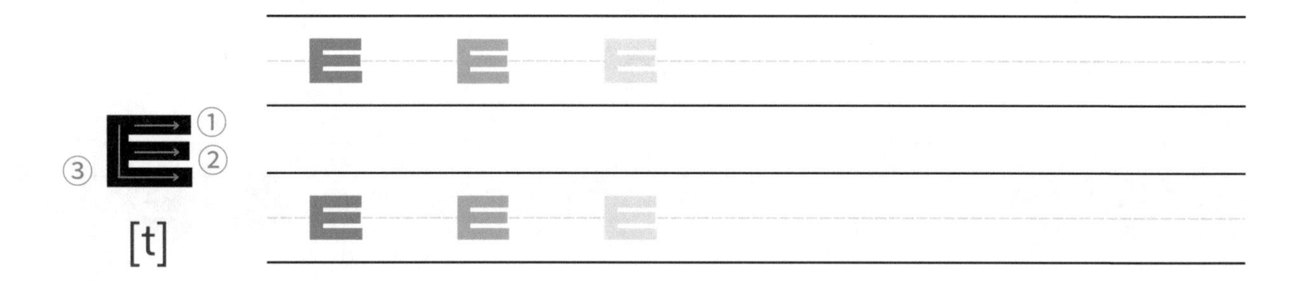

Combine 'ㅌ' (티읕 [tee eut]) with the basic vowels. Trace, write, and read them out loud.

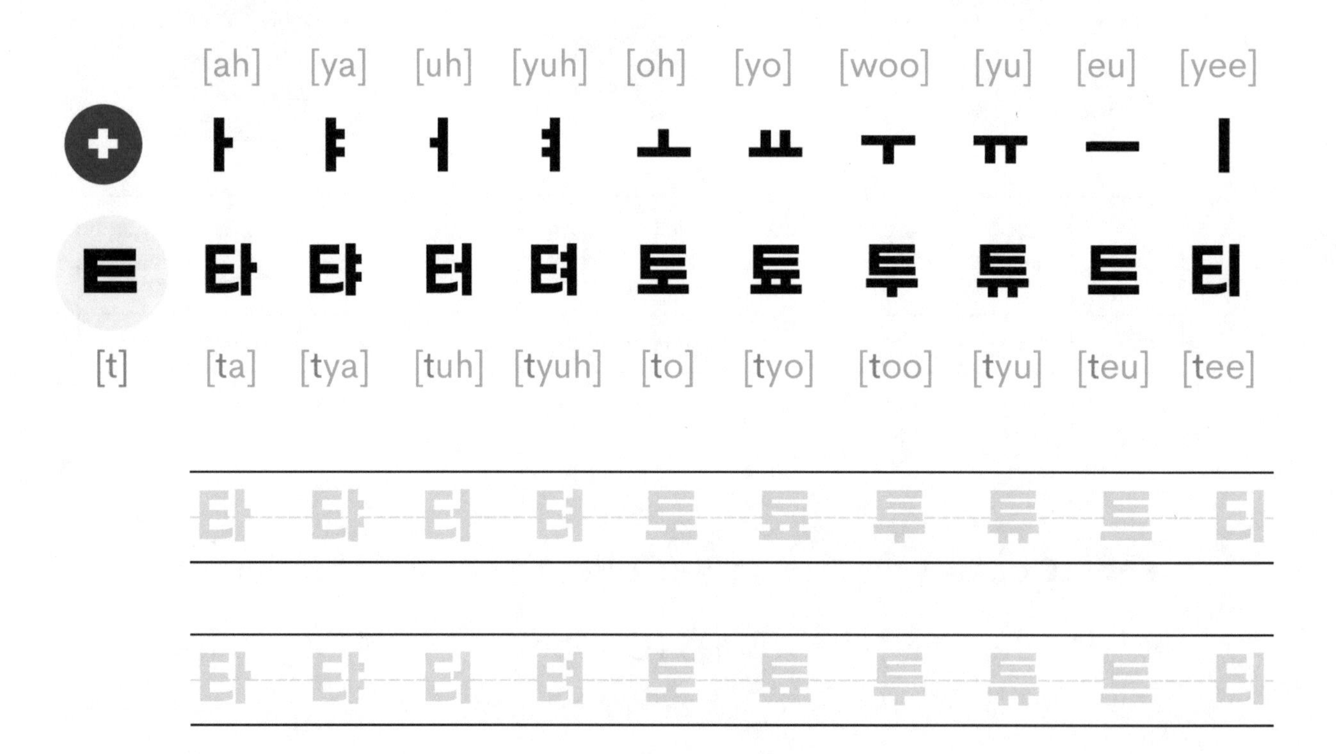

■ Choose the correct word from the word bank below for each picture, and write it to complete the words.

기	
gi	ta

	요	일
to	yo	il

	림
teu	lim

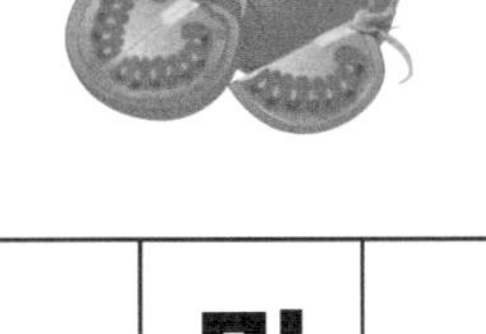

	마	
to	ma	to

	널
tuh	null

파	
pa	tee

트림 (Burp)　　터널 (Tunnel)　　토요일 (Saturday)

파티 (Party)　　기타 (Guitar)　　토마토 (Tomato)

Date: / /

Basic consonant: ㅍ 피읖 [pee eup]

The 'ㅍ' (피읖 [pee eup]) is pronounced similar to a hard [p] at the beginning of words or syllables. Trace and write 'ㅍ'.

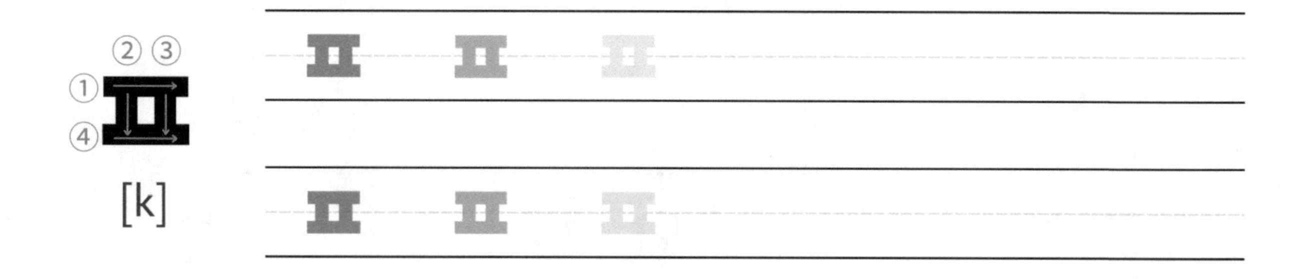

Combine 'ㅍ' (피읖 [pee eup]) with the basic vowels. Trace, write, and read them out loud.

	[ah]	[ya]	[uh]	[yuh]	[oh]	[yo]	[woo]	[yu]	[eu]	[yee]
+	ㅏ	ㅑ	ㅓ	ㅕ	ㅗ	ㅛ	ㅜ	ㅠ	ㅡ	ㅣ
ㅍ	파	퍄	퍼	펴	포	표	푸	퓨	프	피
[p]	[pa]	[pya]	[puh]	[pyuh]	[po]	[pyo]	[poo]	[pyu]	[peu]	[pee]

파 퍄 퍼 펴 포 표 푸 퓨 프 피

파 퍄 퍼 펴 포 표 푸 퓨 프 피

■ Choose the correct word from the word bank below for each picture, and write it to complete the words.

파리 (Fly) 피아노 (Piano) 포도 (Grape)

샴푸 (Shampoo) 피부 (Skin) 양파 (Onion)

Basic consonant: ㅎ 히읗 [hee eut]

The 'ㅎ' (히읗 [hee eut]) is pronounced similar to a hard [h] at the beginning of words or syllables. Trace and write 'ㅎ'.

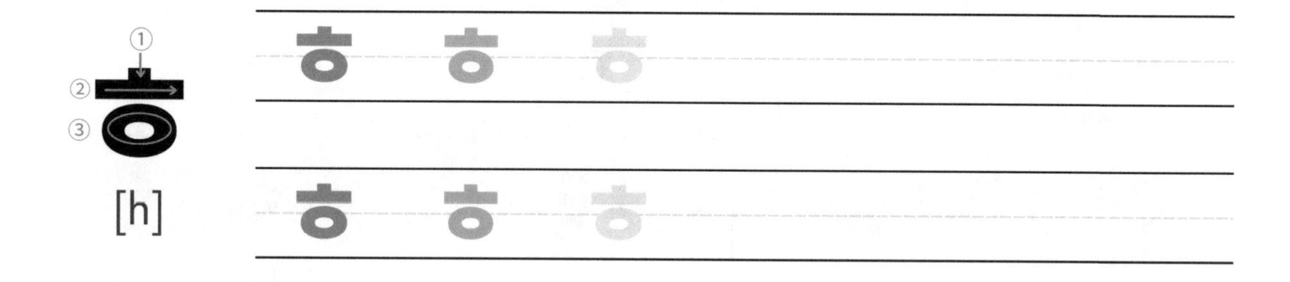

Combine 'ㅎ' (히읗 [hee eut]) with the basic vowels. Trace, write, and read them out loud.

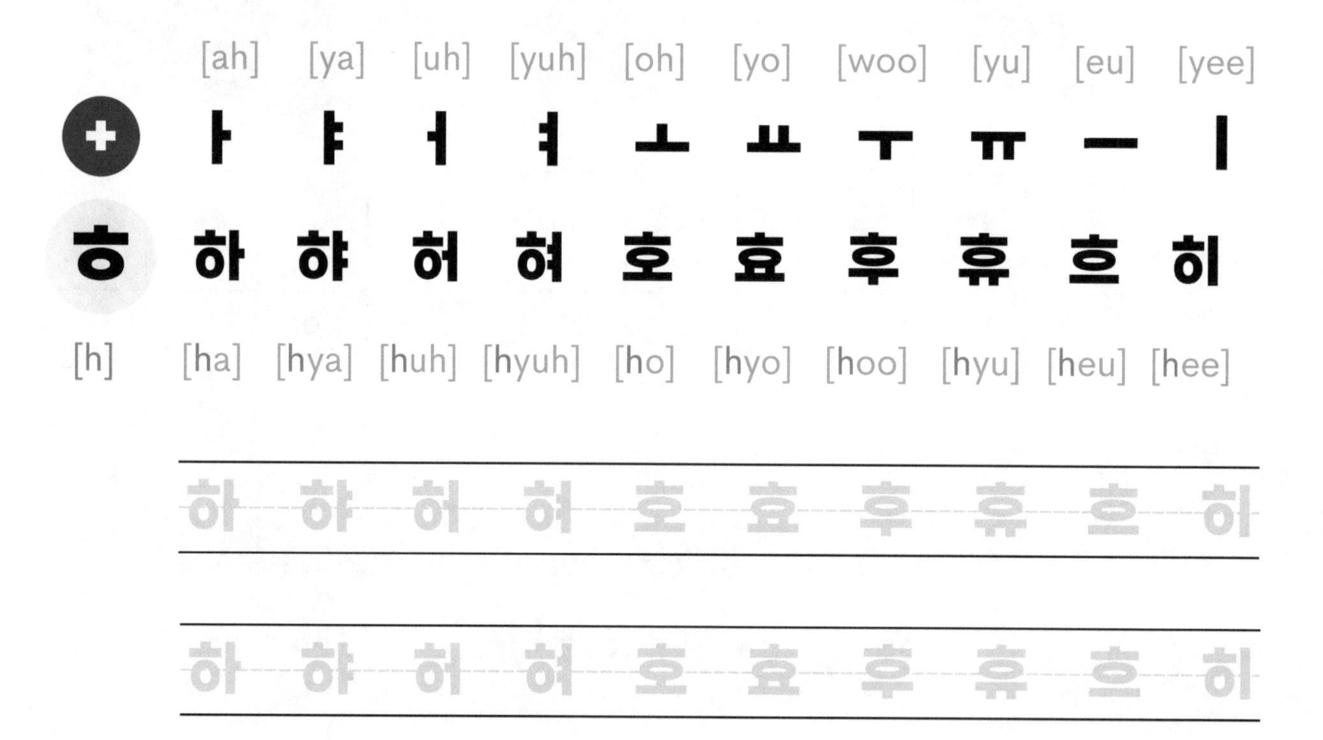

■ Choose the correct word from the word bank below for each picture, and write it to complete the words.

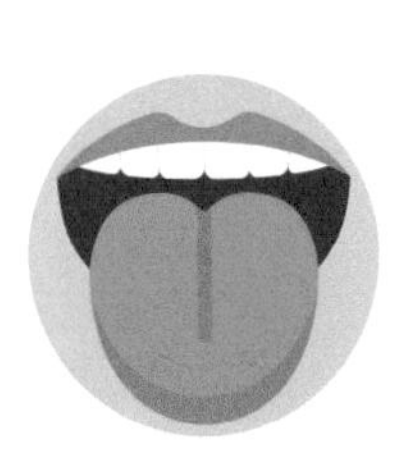

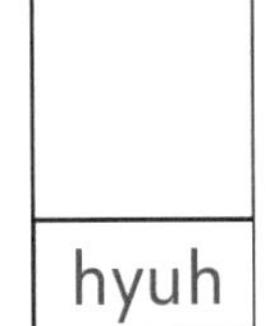

hyuh

	추
hoo	choo

훌	라		프
hool	la	hoo	peu

	수
ho	soo

오	
oh	hoo

	랑	이
ho	rang	yee

후추 (Black Pepper) 호랑이 (Tiger) 오후 (Afternoon)

훌라후프 (Hula hoop) 혀 (Tongue) 호수 (Lake)

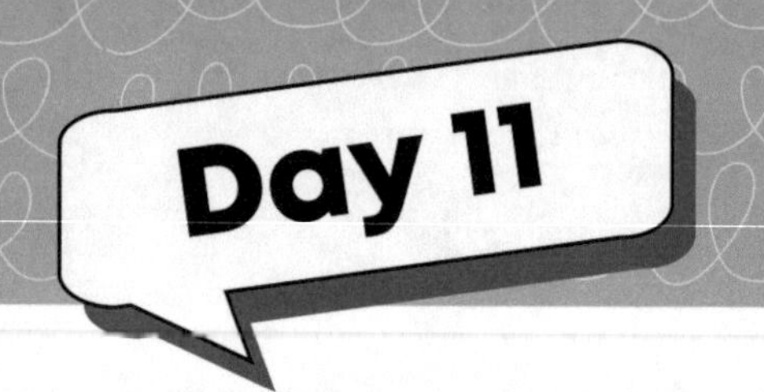

Date: / /

Doubled Consonants

In Korean, there are five double consonants: 'ㄲ,' 'ㄸ,' 'ㅃ,' 'ㅆ,' and 'ㅉ.' These should be pronounced with more emphasis and strength than their single versions. Try pronouncing them out loud, focusing on the increased effort to feel the difference.

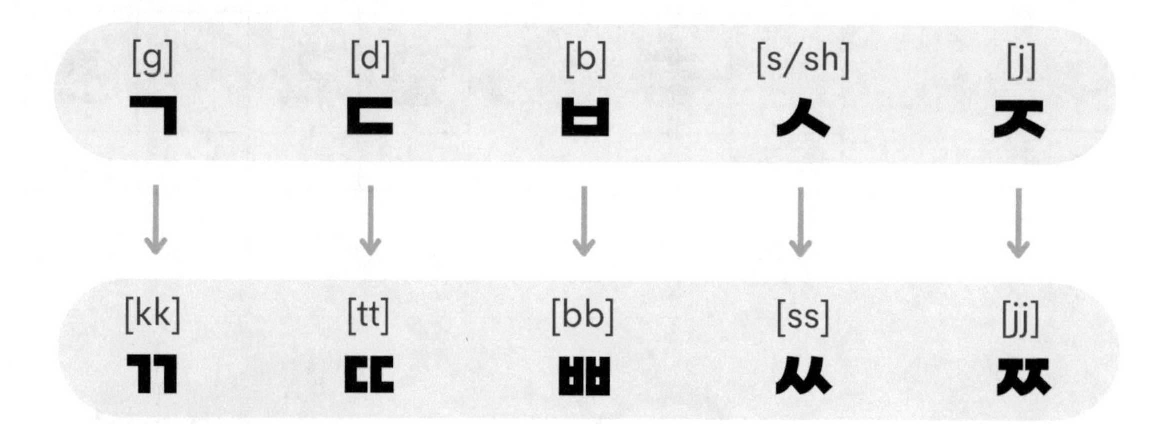

■ Trace the letters while saying each word.

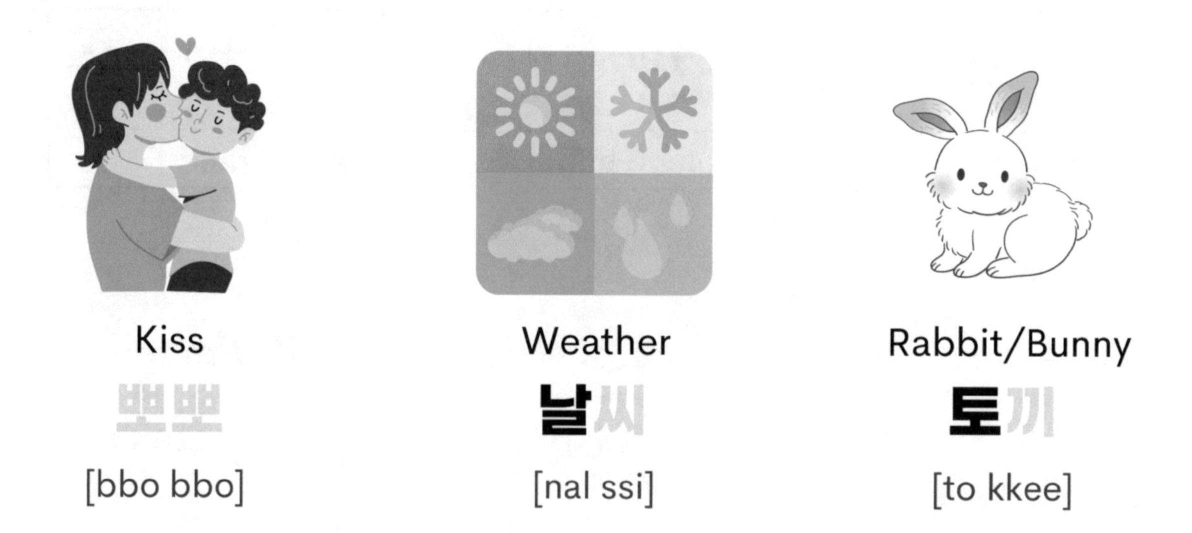

Match the pictures and their names in Korean.

Writing Double Consonants

Trace and write the words while saying each word out loud.
Pay special attention to the double consonants.

Bread: 빵 [bbang]

빵 빵 빵

Gum: 껌 [ggum]

껌 껌 껌

Daughter: 딸 [ttal]

딸 딸 딸

Sprout: 새싹 [se ssak]

새싹 새싹 새싹

Dad: 아빠 [a bba]

아빠 아빠

Honey: 꿀 [kkool]

꿀 꿀

Land: 땅 [ttang]

땅 땅

Roots: 뿌리 [bboo lee]

뿌리 뿌리

Toad: 두꺼비 [doo kkuh bee]

두꺼비 두꺼비

Date: / /

Final consonant: ㄱ [g] / [k]

The 'ㄱ' (기역 [gi yeok]) sounds somewhere between [g] and [k] when it's at the end of a syllable, as a final consonant (받침 [bat-chim]). Trace the words below as you read them out loud.

가족

Family
[ga jok]

약속

Promise
[yak sok]

국수

Noodles
[gook soo]

트럭

Truck
[teu ruhk]

■ Write the words in Korean and complete the puzzles. You can find the word from the word bank below if you need help.

축하　악기　수박　약속　축구　음악　약국　박수

Final consonant: ㄴ [n]

The 'ㄴ' (니은 [nee eun]) sounds like [n] at the end of a syllable as a final consonant (받침 [bat-chim]). Trace the words below as you read out loud.

우산

Umbrella
[woo san]

[사] + [ㄴ]

산

만두

Dumpling
[man doo]

눈

Snow
[□noon]

반지

Ring
[ban jee]

■ Write the words in Korean and complete the puzzles. You can find the word from the word bank below if you need help.

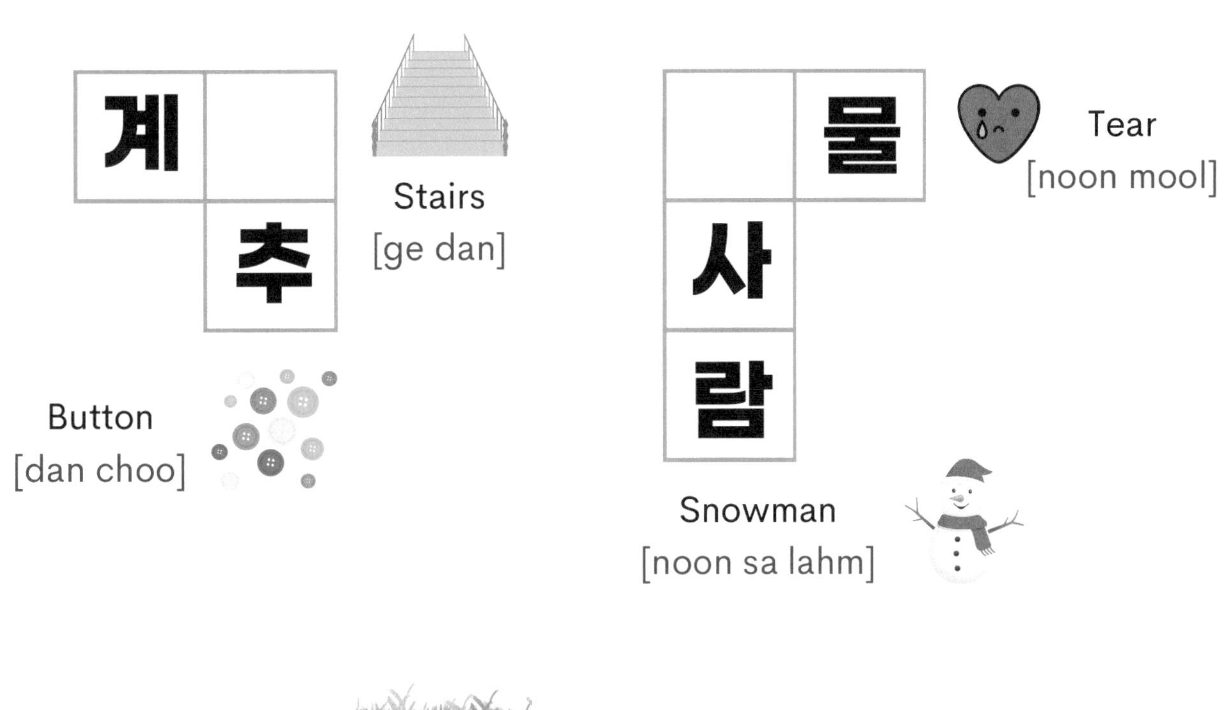

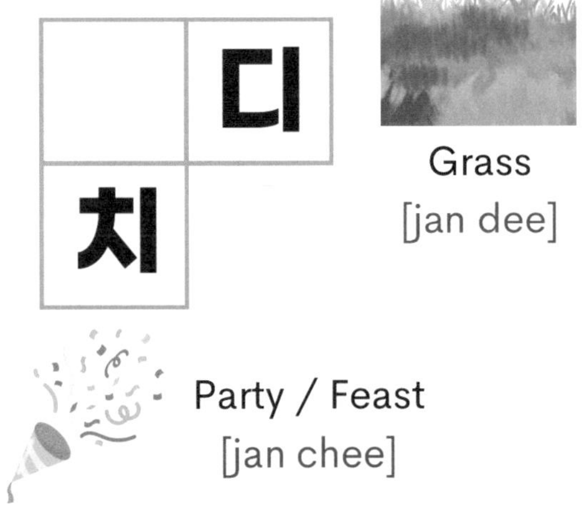

Stroll
[san chaek]

눈사람 등산 단추 산책 눈물 잔디 계단 잔치

Date: / /

Final consonant: ㄷ [d] / [t]

The 'ㄷ' (디귿 [dee geut]) is pronounced somewhere between [d] and [t] when it appears at the end of a syllable, acting as a final consonant (받침 [bat-chim]). Trace the words listed below and read them out loud.

숟가락

Spoon
[soot ga rak]

돋보기

Magnifier
[dot bo gi]

해돋이

Sunrise
[hae dot yee]

턱받이

Bib
[tuhk bat yee]

■ Match the pictures representing the verbs with the final consonant of 'ㄷ' (디귿 [dee geut]) and their Korean words.

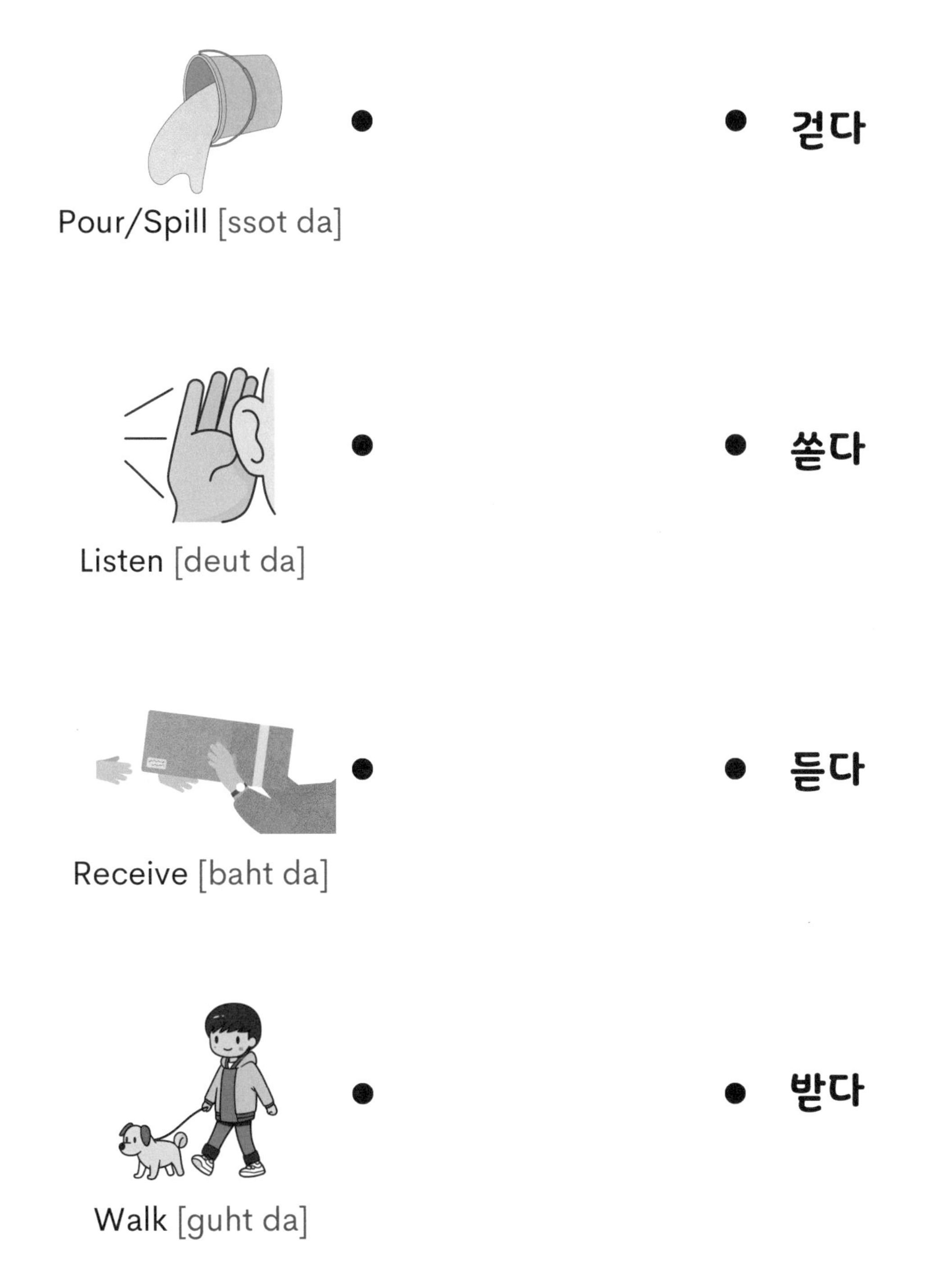

Final consonant: ㄹ [r] / [l]

The 'ㄹ' (리을 [lee eul]) is pronounced like [r] or [l] at the end of a syllable as a final consonant (받침 [bat-chim]). Trace the words below as you read out loud.

Grandma [hal muh nee]

Grandpa [hal ah buh jee]

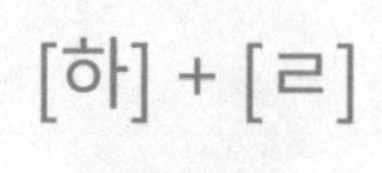

Bee
[buhl]

Sky
[ha neul]

물고기

Fish
[mool go gi]

■ Circle the words from the word bank. You can find them in horizontal and vertical directions: → ← ↑ ↓

국	신	기	국	국	초	날	매	력	신
자	력	씨	신	초	승	달	양	달	리
매	력	력	력	리	양	신	신	날	기
자	양	리	달	력	말	승	리	갈	국
갈	리	신	발	기	승	찰	신	찰	씨
달	찰	찰	경	날	씨	갈	경	양	경
양	달	신	발	발	초	승	달	달	자
매	리	기	갈	신	국	력	신	국	발
씨	기	매	력	초	승	씨	날	말	자
리	자	갈	기	씨	날	양	기	경	국

달력 [dal ryeok] (Calendar)
달리기 [dal lee gi] (Running)
경찰 [gyeong chal] (Police officer)
발자국 [bal ja gook] (Footstep)
갈매기 [gal mae gi] (Seagull)
양말 [yang mal] (Socks)
날씨 [nal ssi] (Weather)
초승달 [cho seung dal] (Crescent moon)

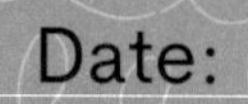

Date: / /

Final consonant: ㅁ [g] / [k]

The 'ㅁ' (미음 [mee eum]) is pronounced like [m] at the end of a syllable as a final consonant (받침 [bat-chim]). Trace the words below as you read out loud.

감자

Potato
[gam ja]

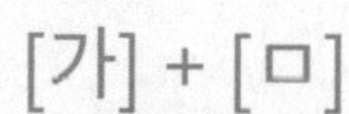

구름

Cloud
[goo reum]

바람

Wind
[ba ram]

잠자리

Dragonfly
[jam ja lee]

■ Write the Korean words with the final consonant 'ㅁ' (미음 [mee-eum]) from the word bank below.

Pot [naem bee]:

____

Bear [gom]:

____

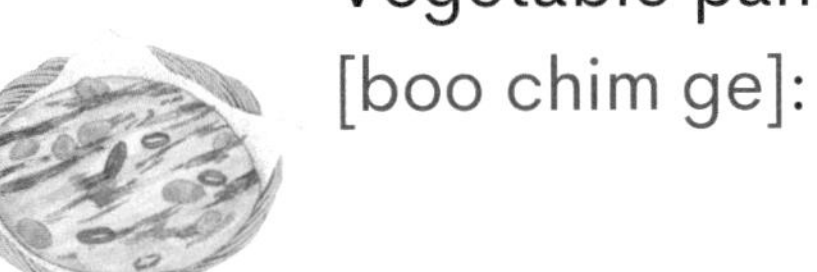

Vegetable pancake [boo chim ge]:

____

Man [nam ja]:

____

Deer [sa seum]:

____

Yawn [ha poom]

____

Bed [chim dae]:

____

Deep-fried food [tui gim]:

____

Salt [so geum]:

____

Flu/Cold [gahm gi]:

____

부침개	소금	튀김	침대	남자
사슴	냄비	하품	감기	곰

Final consonant: ㅂ [b] / [p]

The 'ㅂ' (비읍 [bee eup]) sounds somewhere between [b] and [p] when it's at the end of a syllable, acting as a final consonant (받침 [bat-chim]). Trace the words below and read them out loud.

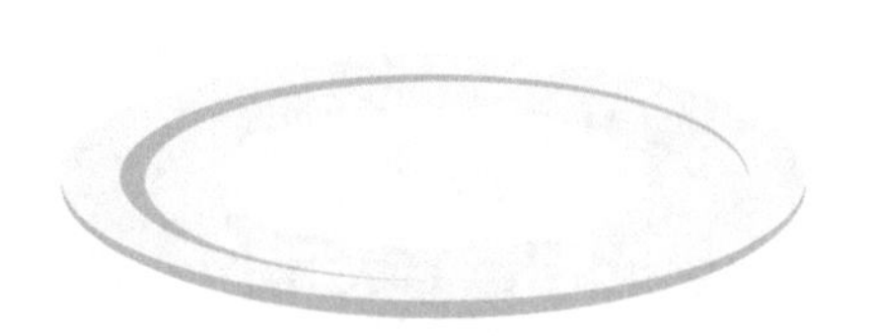

Plate
[juhp shee]

[저] + [ㅂ]

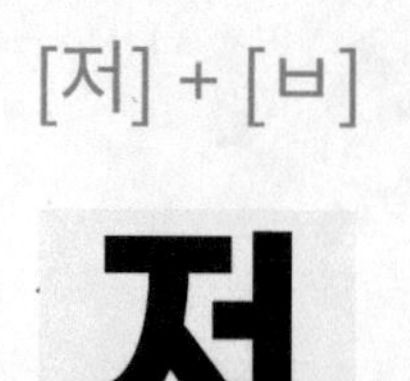

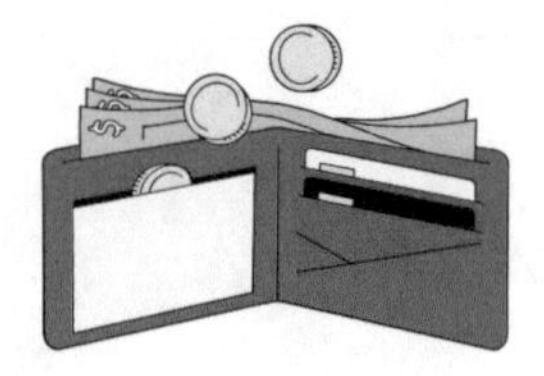

Purse/Wallet
[jee gap]

Bee bim bap

Cup
[kuhp]

■ Circle all the words with the **final consonant** of 'ㅂ'.

바나나
[ba na na]

버스
[buh seu]

보트
[bo teu]

팝콘
[pap kon]

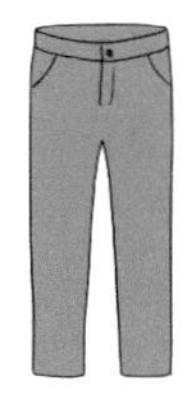

바지
[ba jee]

집
[jip]

버터
[buh tuh]

장갑
[jang gahp]

구급차
[goo geup cha]

밥
[bap]

버섯
[buh seot]

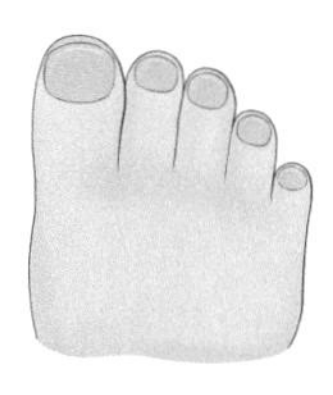

발가락
[bal gah rak]

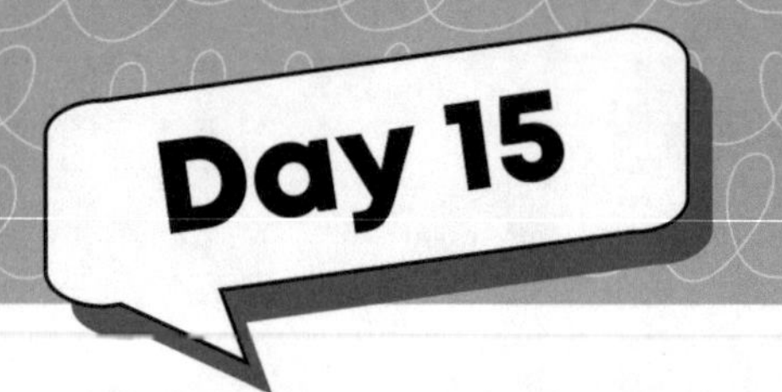

Date: / /

Final consonant: ㅇ [ng]

The 'ㅇ' (이응 [yee eung]) is silent when it precedes a vowel at the beginning of a syllable and is pronounced like [ng] when it's used as a final consonant (받침 [bat-chim]). Trace the words below and read them out loud.

유리병

Glass Bottle
[yu lee byeong]

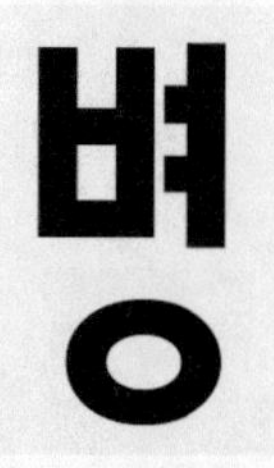

강아지

Puppy
[gang ah jee]

배낭

Backpack
[bae nang]

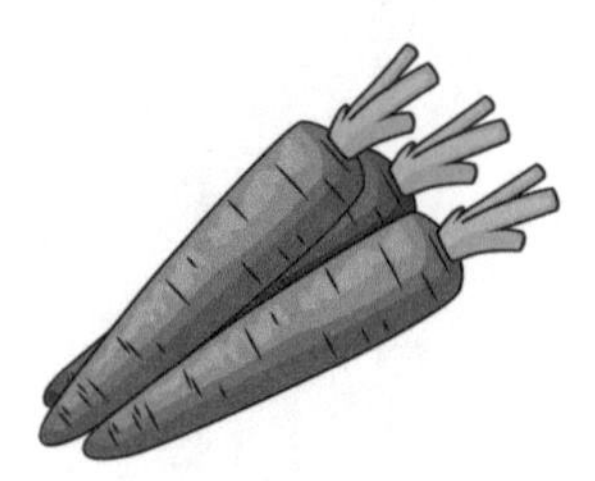

당근

Carrot
[dang geun]

■ Fill in the crossword with Korean words for each English clue in the Across & Down sections, using the word bank for hints.

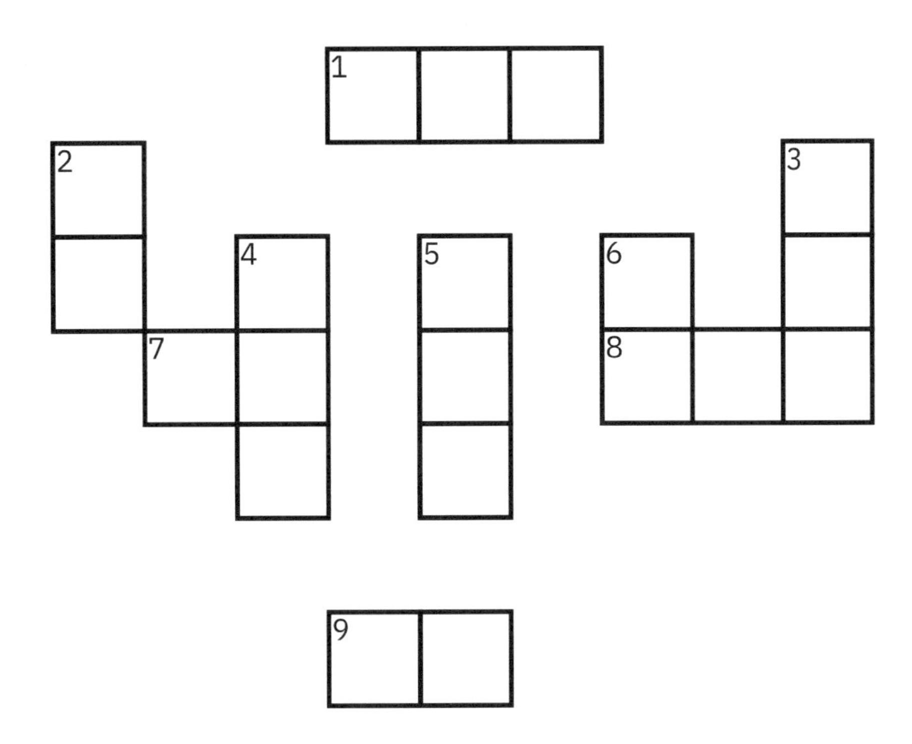

Across

1. Kitty [go yang yee]
7. Bag [ga bang]
8. (Electric) Fan [suhn poong gi]
9. Shark [sang uh]

Down

2. Window [chang moon]
3. Airplane [bee haeng gi]
4. Fire truck [so bang cha]
5. Puppy [gang ah jee]
6. Balloon [poong suhn]

창문 선풍기 소방차 고양이 상어 강아지 풍선 비행기 가방

Final consonant family of 'ㄱ'

The consonants 'ㄱ' [g], 'ㅋ' [k], and 'ㄲ' [gg] each have distinct sounds at the beginning of words or syllables. However, when they appear at the end of a syllable as a final consonant (받침 [bat-chim]), they all sound like 'ㄱ,' between [g] and [k]. Trace the words below and read them out loud.

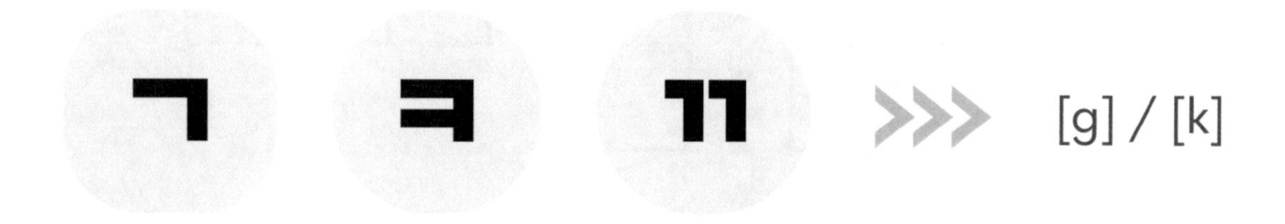

Watermelon
[soo bak]

Kitchen
[boo uhk]

낚시

Fishing
[nak shee]

■ Circle the words from the word bank. You can find them in horizontal and vertical directions: → ← ↑ ↓ The first is the example.

음	구	탁	음	낚	부	떡	축	음	녘
부	더	이	낚	시	수	엌	엌	축	득
식	탁	깎	옥	음	질	낚	더	부	구
볶	음	밥	깎	엌	다	음	탁	이	옥
더	옥	더	밥	깎	밥	녘	옥	수	수
시	엌	음	떡	닦	떡	음	구	식	음
득	닦	국	깎	다	이	축	부	낚	부
볶	시	녘	질	해	축	구	낚	낚	엌
음	식	더	음	부	질	다	더	득	밥
수	국	득	낚	이	부	닦	떡	볶	이

국수 [gook soo] (Noodles)

떡볶이 [ttuk bok yee]

옥수수 [ok soo soo] (Corn)

깎다 [kkak da] (To peel)

부엌 [boo uhk] (Kitchen)

축구 [chook goo] (Football)

닦다 [dak da] (To wipe)

식탁 [shik tak] (Dining table)

Day 16

Date: / /

Final consonant family of 'ㅂ'

The consonants 'ㅂ' [b] and 'ㅍ' [p] have distinct pronunciations at the beginning of words or syllables. However, when they come at the end of a syllable as a final consonant (받침 [bat-chim]), both are pronounced as 'ㅂ,' which sounds somewhere between [b] and [p]. Trace the words below and read them out loud.

   [b] / [p]

팝콘

Popcorn
[pab kon]

입술

Lips
[yip sool]

옆집

Next door
[yuhp jip]

무릎

Knee
[moo reup]

■ Write the Korean word corresponding to each picture and its English description using the words in the word bank.

Ambulance [goo geup cha]: ________________

Maple leaf [dan poong yip]: ________________

Apron [ap chi ma]: ________________

Leaf [yip]: ________________

Fingernail [sohn tohp]: ________________

Mouth [yip]: ________________

Gloves [jang gap]: ________________

Shovel [sahp]: ________________

Plate [juhp shee]: ________________

Knee [moo reup]: ________________

앞치마 구급차 잎 입 장갑

접시 무릎 삽 손톱 단풍잎

Final consonant family of ‘ㄷ’

When the consonants 'ㄷ' [d], 'ㅅ' [s], 'ㅆ' [ss], 'ㅈ' [j], 'ㅊ' [ch], and 'ㅌ' [t] are at the end of a syllable as a final consonant (받침 [bat-chim]), they are all pronounced similarly to 'ㄷ,' with a sound that falls between [d] and [t]. Trace the words listed below and read them out loud.

Spoon [soot gah rak]

Mushroom [buh suht]

Went [ghat ta]

낮잠

Nap
[nat jahm]

꽃

Flower
[kkot]

끝

End
[ggeut]

벚꽃

Cherry blossom
[buht kkot]

턱받이

Bib
[tuhk bat yee]

좋다

Good
[jot ta]

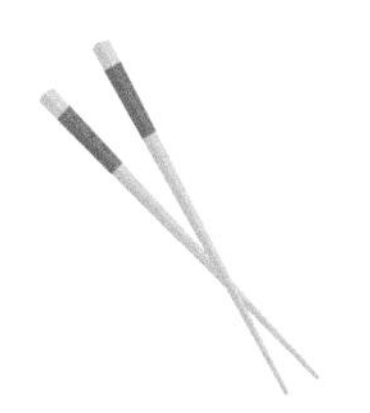

젓가락

Chopsticks
[juht ga rak]

찾다

Find
[chat ta]

같다

Same
[ghat ta]

Date: / /

Vocabulary review: Final Consonants

Write the Korean words with the final consonants we learned from the word bank below.

Stroll [san chaek]:

____

Promise [yak sok]:

____

Magnifier [dot bo gi]:

____

Socks [yang mal]:

____

Pharmacy [yak gook]:

____

Potato [gam ja]:

____

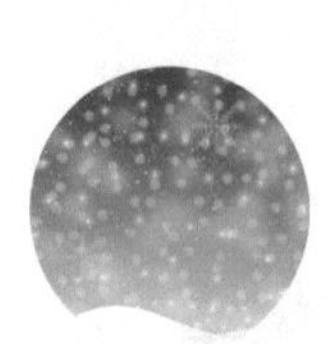

Snow [noon]:

____

Flu/Cold [gahm gi]:

____

감기	약속	산책	감자
약국	돋보기	양말	눈

Gloves [jang gap]: ____________________

Backpack [bae nang]: ____________________

Mushroom [buh seot]: ____________________

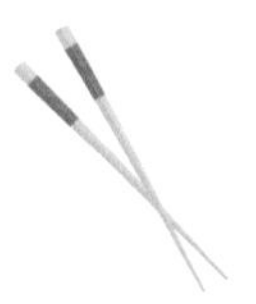

Chopsticks [juht ga rak]: ____________________

Lips [yip sool]: ____________________

Kitchen [boo uhk]: ____________________

Shark [sang uh]: ____________________

Leaf [yip]: ____________________

Bed [chim dae]: ____________________

House [jip]: ____________________

Flower [kkot]: ____________________

Kitty [go yang yee]: ____________________

젓가락	장갑	잎	집	배낭	부엌
꽃	상어	고양이	버섯	입술	침대

■ Fill in the crossword with Korean words for each English clue in the Across & Down sections, using the word bank for hints.

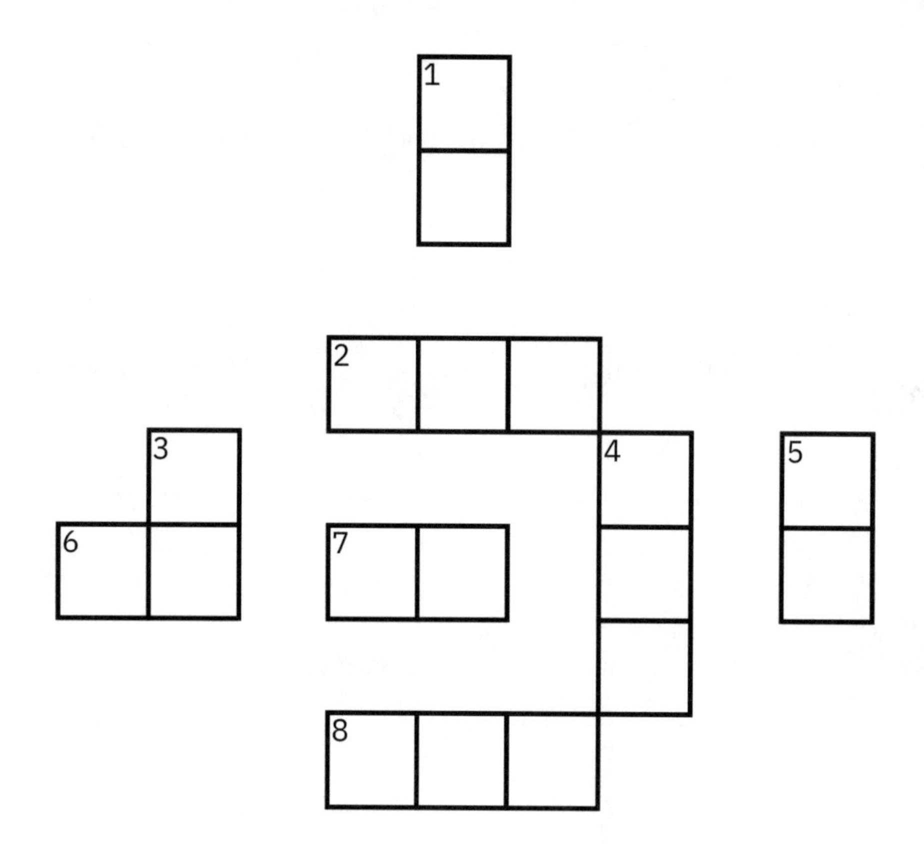

Across

2. Rough sketch [meet geu lim]
6. Went [ghat ta]
7. Milk cow [juht so]
8. Chopsticks [juht ga rak]

Down

1. Sunlight [haet bit]
3. Pile Up [ssat ta]
4. Magnifier [dot bo gi]
5. Floral leaf [kkot yip]

갔다 젓가락 젖소 돋보기 꽃잎 밑그림 쌓다 햇빛

■ Circle the words from the word bank. You can find them in horizontal and vertical directions: → ← ↑ ↓ The first is the example.

낮	가	꽃	벚	벚	같	락	같	낮	좋
기	벚	버	좋	다	좋	잠	기	숟	섯
기	꽃	낮	버	락	잠	낮	좋	벚	레
레	꽃	레	숟	레	꽃	섯	왔	기	벚
가	다	숟	가	좋	쓰	레	받	기	왔
레	낮	섯	락	왔	받	섯	숟	버	섯
쓰	다	받	기	다	낮	섯	가	낮	다
왔	꽃	락	좋	레	레	다	받	받	다
왔	낮	왔	같	쓰	받	같	숟	꽃	다
섯	좋	섯	왔	쓰	기	레	기	레	벚

벚꽃 [buht kkot] (Cherry Blossom)

같다 [□ghat ta] (Same)

숟가락 [soot ga rak] (Spoon)

버섯 [buh suht] (Mushroom)

좋다 [jot ta] (Good)

왔다 [wat ta] (Came/Arrived)

낮잠 [nat jahm] (Nap)

쓰레받기 [sseu reh bat gi] (Dustpan)

Date: / /

Combined Vowels - 'ㅐ' and 'ㅔ'

The combined vowels 'ㅐ' and 'ㅔ' are formed as follows:

ㅏ [ah] + ㅣ [yee] = ㅐ [ae]

ㅓ [uh] + ㅣ [yee] = ㅔ [e]

'ㅐ' is pronounced as [æ], similar to the 'a' in "bag," and 'ㅔ' sounds more like [ɛ] or [e], as in 'e' in "bed." In writing, 'ㅐ' is written as [ae] and 'ㅔ' as [e]. Practice by saying the words below out loud using these vowels, then trace them.

노래
Song
[noh rae]

무지개
Rainbow
[moo jee gae]

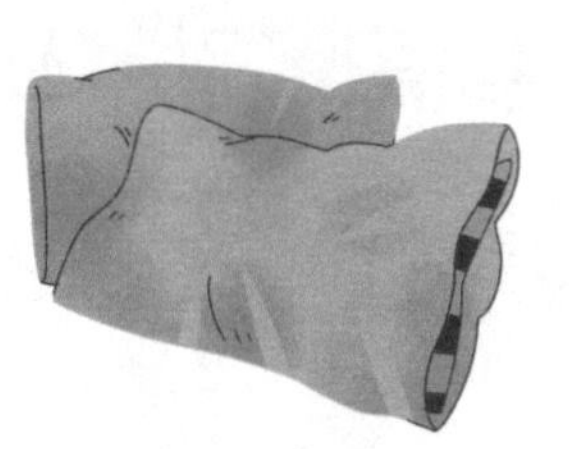

베개
Pillow
[be gae]

세수
To wash face
[se soo]

■ All the words listed include the combined vowel, 'ㅐ' [ae] or 'ㅔ' [e]. Circle the ones you know, and trace all the words.

새우 [sae woo]
Shrimp

개구리 [gae goo lee]
Frog

세모 [se mo]
Triangle

냄비 [naem bee]
Pot

테니스 [te nee seu]
Tennis

동생 [dong saeng]
Younger Sibling

메뉴 [me nyu]
Menu

침대 [chim dae]
Bed

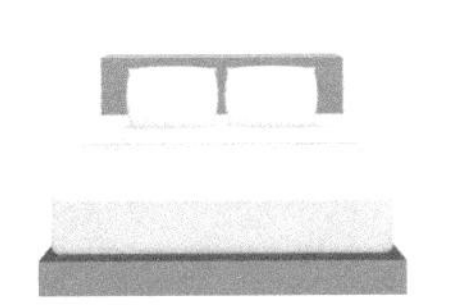

케이크 [ke yee keu]
Cake

배낭 [bae nang]
Backpack

채소 [chae so]
Vegetable

세차 [se cha]
Car wash

Combined Vowels - 'ㅖ' and 'ㅒ'

The combined vowels 'ㅖ' and 'ㅒ' are formed as follows:

ㅕ [yuh] + ㅣ [yee] = ㅖ [ye]

ㅑ [ya] + ㅣ [yee] = ㅒ [ye]

'ㅖ' sounds similar to the 'ye' in "yes," while 'ㅒ' is closer to [jɛ]. The difference is minimal, and both 'ㅖ' and 'ㅒ' sound like [ye]. Practice pronouncing the words below out loud using these vowels, then trace them.

계란

Egg
[ge ran]

시계

Clock/Watch
[shee ge]

얘기

Story
[ye gi]
* Short form of '이야기' [yee ya gi]

걔

That kid/person
[ge]

■ Find the words with the combined vowel, 'ㅖ' [ye] or 'ㅒ' [ye], and write them under each picture.

World [se ge]

____

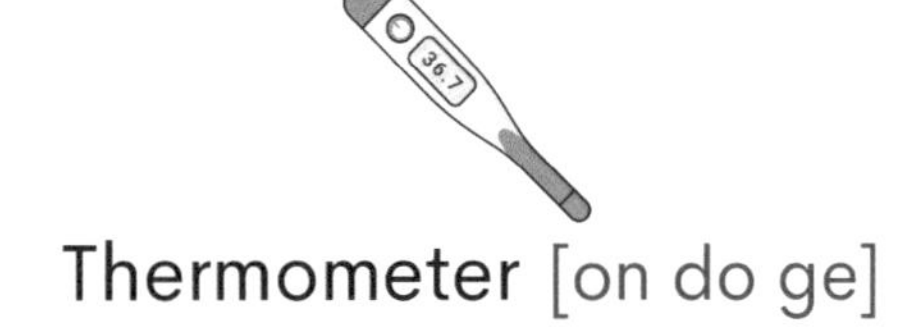

Thermometer [on do ge]

____

This kid [ye]

____

Seasons [ge juhl]

____

Calculator [ge san gi]

____

Order/Turn [cha re]

____

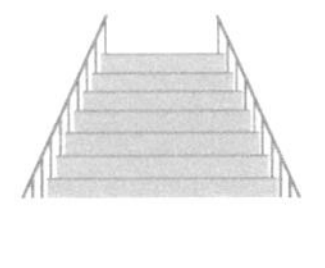

Stairs [ge dan]

____

Continuously [ge sok]

____

Paper money [jee pe]

____

계속 계절 온도계 얘 세계 차례 지폐 계단 계산기

Date: / /

Combined Vowels - 'ㅘ' and 'ㅝ'

The combined vowels 'ㅘ' and 'ㅝ' are formed as follows:

ㅗ [oh] + ㅏ [ah] = ㅘ [wa]

ㅜ [woo] + ㅓ [uh] = ㅝ [wo]

'ㅘ' is pronounced similar to the [wa] in "wow," but 'ㅝ' is closer to the [wo] in "won." Practice pronouncing the words below out loud using these vowels, then trace them.

와플

Waffle
[wa peul]

사과

Apple
[sa gwa]

공원

Park
[gong won]

병원

Hospital
[byeong won]

■ Find the words with the combined vowel, 'ㅘ' [wa] or 'ㅝ' [wo], and write them under each picture.

Cracker/Cookie [gwa ja]

____

Fruit [gwa il]

____

Monkey [won soong yee]

____

Crown [wang gwan]

____

Painter [hwa ga]

____

Tae Kwon Do

____

Scientist [gwa hak ja]

____

Tower [ta wo]

____

Kindergarten [yu chee won]

____

화가 과자 과학자 태권도 과일 타워 유치원 왕관 원숭이

Combined Vowels - 'ㅟ' and 'ㅢ'

The combined vowels 'ㅟ' and 'ㅢ' are formed as follows:

ㅜ [woo] + ㅣ [yee] = ㅟ [wee]

ㅡ [eu] + ㅣ [yee] = ㅢ [eui]

'ㅟ' is pronounced like the 'wee' in "week." 'ㅢ' is trickier; traditionally, it combines the sounds [eu] and [i], quickly blending to sound somewhat like [euі]. Practice pronouncing the words below out loud using these vowels, then trace them.

Switch [seu wi chee] | Mouse [gwee] | Chair [eui ja] | Doctor [eui sa]

■ Find the words with the combined vowels 'ㅟ' [wee] or 'ㅢ' [euii] and write them under each picture.

Scissors [ga wee]

____

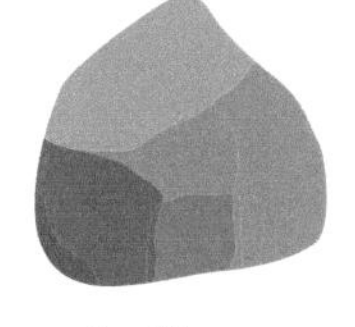
Rock [ba wee]

____

Ear [gwee]

____

Penguin [peng gween]

____

Dice [joo sa wee]

____

Bat [bak jwee]

____

Goose [guh wee]

____

Pattern [moo neui]

____

Determination
[eui jee]

____

의지 귀 주사위 펭귄 가위 박쥐 거위 바위 무늬

Combined Vowels - 'ㅚ', 'ㅙ', and 'ㅞ'

The combined vowels 'ㅚ,' 'ㅙ,' and 'ㅞ' are formed as follows:

ㅗ [oh]	+	ㅣ [yee]	=	외 [oe]
ㅗ [oh]	+	ㅐ [□ae]	=	왜 [wae]
ㅜ [woo]	+	ㅔ [e]	=	웨 [we]

The combined vowels 'ㅚ,' 'ㅙ,' and 'ㅞ' have unique written forms, but in real conversation, they are all pronounced closely to [weh] or [we], as in 'Western.' Practice saying the words below out loud using these combined vowels, then trace them.

외동	왜	스웨터
Only Child [weh dong]	Why [weh]	Sweater [seu weh tuh]

■ Find the words with the combined vowels 'ㅚ,' 'ㅙ,' and 'ㅞ' and write them under each picture.

Pig [dwe jee]

____

Monster [gwe mool]

____

Best [chwe go]

____

Key [yeol swe]

____

Printing [in swe]

____

Meeting [hwe eui]

____

It's okay [gwen chan ah]

____

Waiter [we yee tuh]

____

Church [gyo hwe]

____

돼지 웨이터 회의 열쇠 괴물 괜찮아 교회 최고 인쇄

■ Fill in the crossword with Korean words for each English clue in the Across & Down sections, using the word bank for hints.

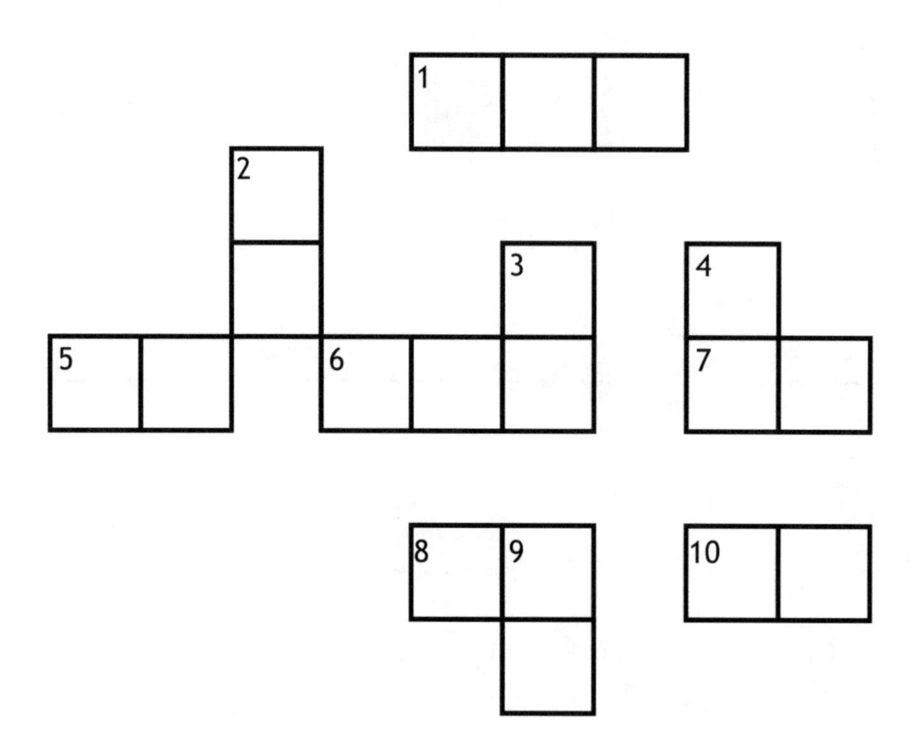

Across

1. Thermometer [on do ge]
5. To wash face [se soo]
6. Rainbow [moo jee gae]
7. Stairs [ge dan]
8. Car wash [se cha]
10. Watch/Clock [shee ge]

Down

2. Continuously [ge sok]
3. Pillow [be gae]
4. World [se ge]
9. Order/Turn [cha re]

세계 계속 베개 온도계 계단 무지개
세수 차례 시계 세차

Circle the words with combined vowels from the word bank. All of them are what we learned. You can find them in horizontal and vertical directions: → ← ↑ ↓

물	사	과	유	괴	사	쇄	열	병	치
괴	위	이	숭	자	병	원	원	치	유
웨	위	원	숭	이	숭	과	웨	원	이
유	치	유	원	이	의	자	치	병	사
열	스	터	웨	위	괴	돼	이	열	위
병	병	물	숭	바	돼	스	유	의	유
물	병	스	웨	터	돼	바	과	원	괴
스	사	병	바	지	웨	괴	자	물	터
치	의	자	스	돼	지	유	의	이	돼
사	스	열	병	열	위	물	위	위	지

병원 (Hospital)

과자 (Cracker)

열쇄 (Key)

바위 (Rock)

의자 (Chair)

의사 (Doctor)

돼지 (Pig)

괴물 (Monster)

스웨터 (Sweater)

유치원 (Kindergarten)

원숭이 (Money)

사과 (Apple)

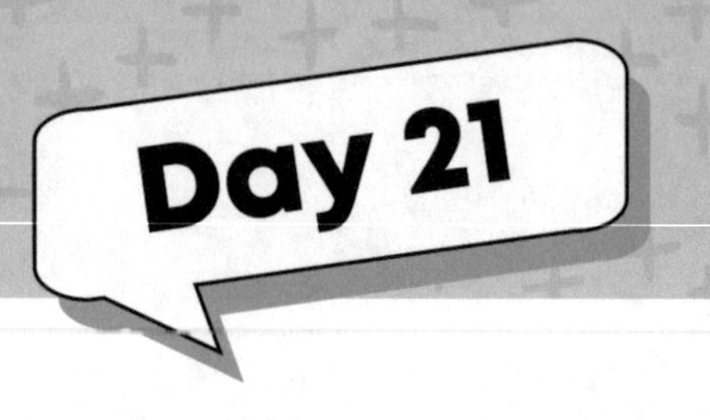

Date: / /

Counting 1–10

Say each word out loud.

하나	**둘**	**셋**	**넷**	**다섯**
[ha na]	[dool]	[set]	[net]	[da suht]

	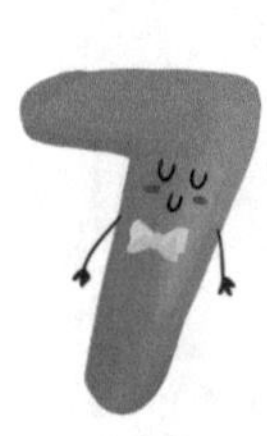			
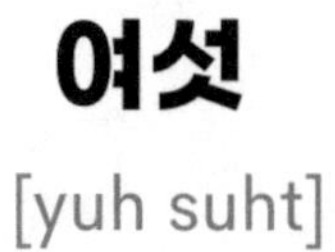 **여섯**	**일곱**	**여덟**	**아홉**	**열**
[yuh suht]	[il gop]	[yuh deol]	[ah hop]	[yeol]

하나	1	●	●
둘	2	●	●
셋	3	●	●
넷	4	●	●
다섯	5	●	●
여섯	6	●	●
일곱	7	●	●
여덟	8	●	●
아홉	9	●	●
열	10	●	●

Matching Numbers

Draw a line to match each number to the Korean words.

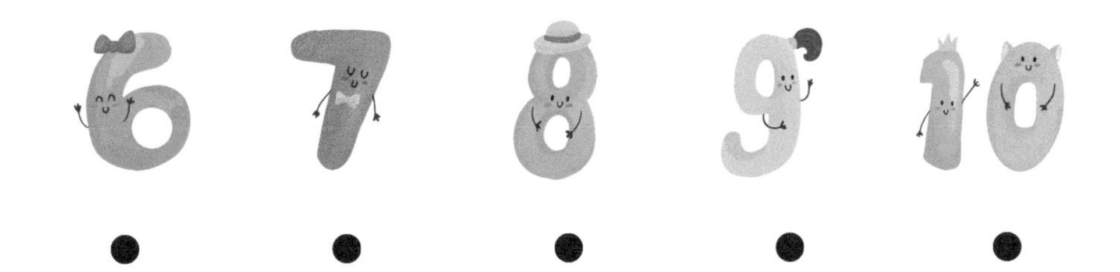

여덟	여섯	열	일곱	아홉
[yuh deol]	[yuh suht]	[yeol]	[il gop]	[ah hop]

Date: / /

Counting the Ice Creams

Write the number that matches the Korean word in each box on the left. Color the correct number of ice creams to show the number written in Korean. The first is the example.

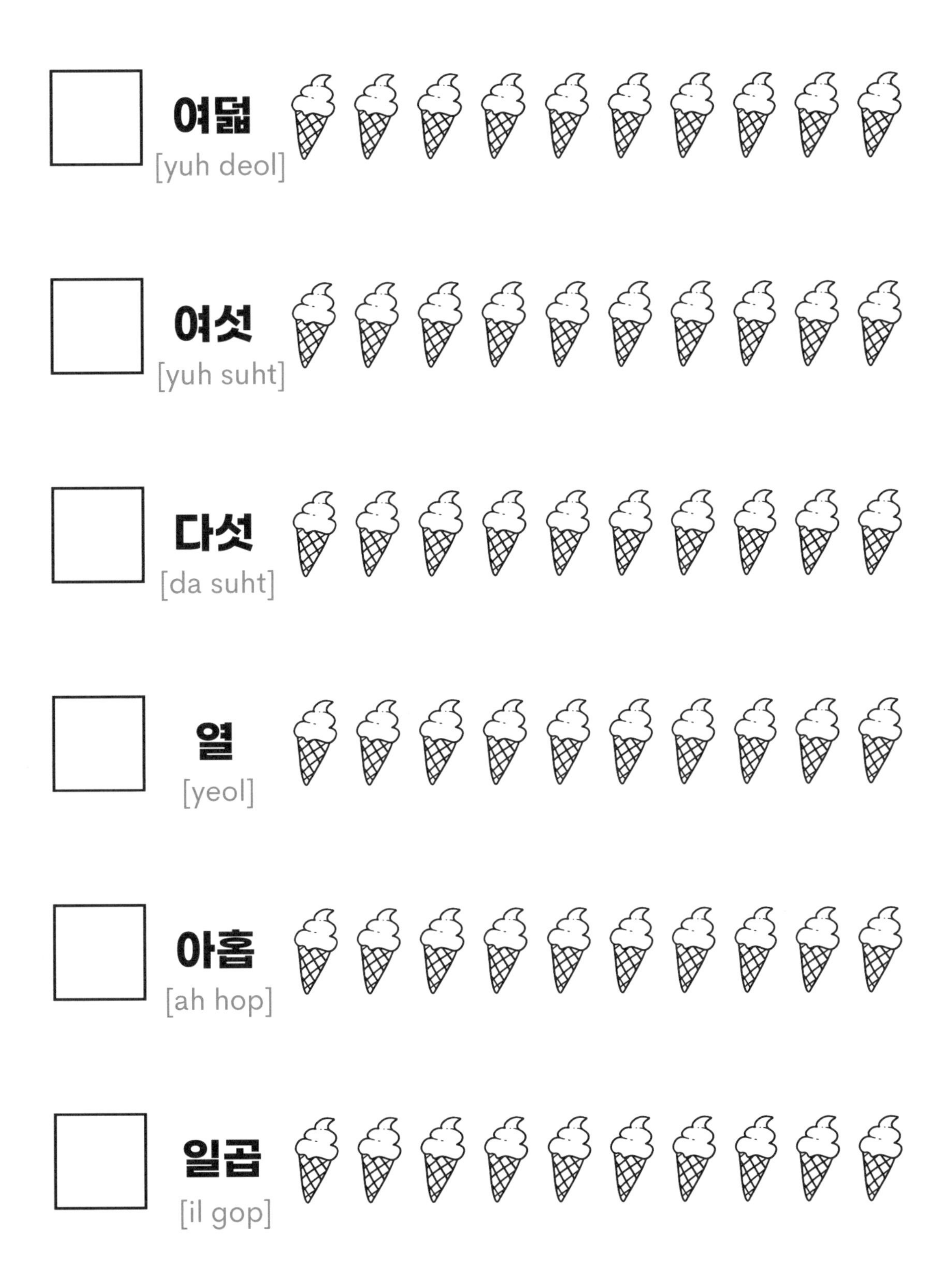
여덟
[yuh deol]
여섯
[yuh suht]
다섯
[da suht]
열
[yeol]
아홉
[ah hop]
일곱
[il gop]

Number 1–10

Pick the Korean words in the box below and write them next to the correct number.

1 ________________

2 ________________

3 ________________

4 ________________

5 ________________

6 ________________

7 ________________

8 ________________

9 ________________

10 ________________

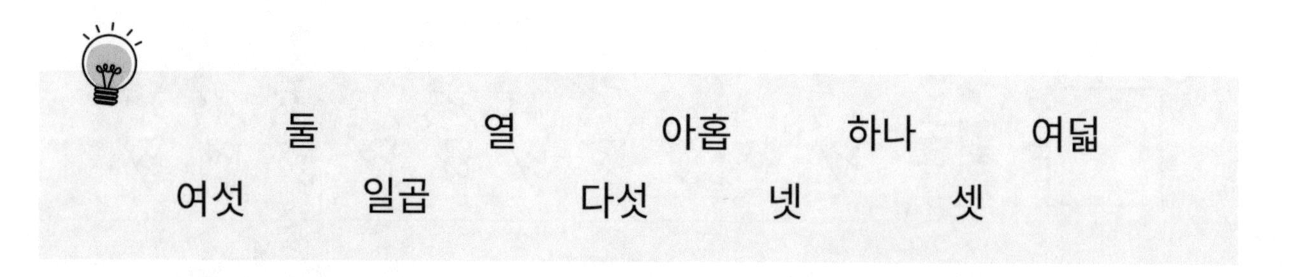

■ Now, write the numbers next to each Korean word. The first one is the example.

[net]	넷	4
[il gop]	일곱	
[set]	셋	
[da suht]	다섯	
[ha na]	하나	
[yuh deol]	여덟	
[yeol]	열	
[yuh suht]	여섯	
[dool]	둘	
[ah hop]	아홉	

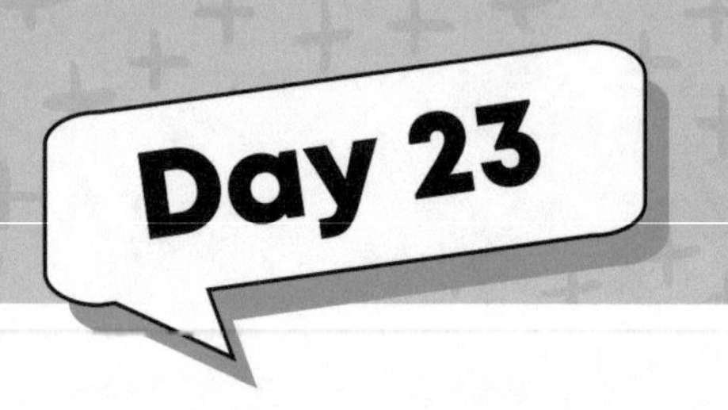

Date: / /

Reading 11-20

Read each word out loud. The numbers 11-20 are 10 (ten: 열 [yeol]) combined with 1-10. You can say '열' [10 yeol] and add the number except 20.

15 = 10 + 5 열다섯
[yeol da suht]

16 = 10 + 6 열여섯
[yeol yuh suht]

17 = 10 + 7 열일곱
[yeol il gop]

18 = 10 + 8 열여덟
[yeol yuh deol]

19 = 10 + 9 열아홉
[yeol ah hop]

20 = 10 + 10 스물
[seu mool]

Matching Numbers 11–20

12	열아홉 [yeol ah hop]
15	열여덟 [yeol yuh deol]
13	열넷 [yeol net]
18	스물 [seu mool]
20	열셋 [yeol set]
16	열일곱 [yeol il gop]
14	열하나 [yeol ha na]
17	열여섯 [yeol yuh suht]
19	열둘 [yeol dool]
11	열다섯 [yeol da suht]

Writing Numbers 11-20

Choose the Korean words for numbers 11-20 from the word bank and write them next to their corresponding number.

11 ____________________
[yeol ha na]

12 ____________________
[yeol dool]

13 ____________________
[yeol set]

14 ____________________
[yeol net]

15 ____________________
[yeol da suht]

16 ____________________
[yeol yuh suht]

17 ____________________
[yeol il gop]

18 ____________________
[yeol yuh deol]

19 ____________________
[yeol ah hop]

20 ____________________
[seu mool]

열일곱 열아홉 열다섯 열하나 열여덟

스물 열셋 열넷 열둘 열여섯

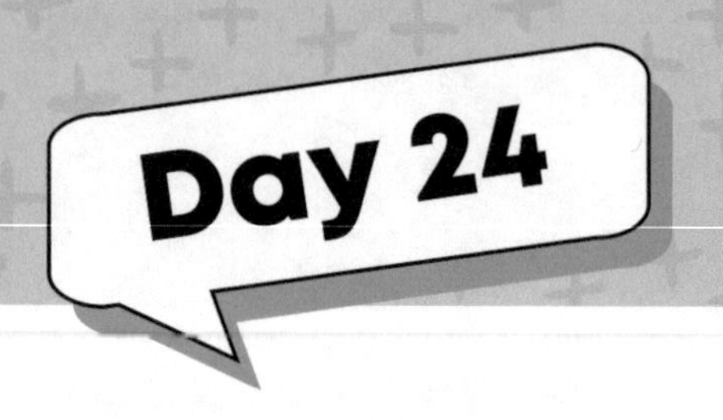

Date: / /

Number 21-30

Read each word out loud. The numbers 21-30 are 20 (twenty: 스물 [seu mool]) combined with 1-10. You can say '스물' [seu mool] and add the number except 30.

스물하나
[seu mool ha na]

스물둘
[seu mool dool]

23 = 20 + 3

스물셋
[seu mool set]

스물넷
[seu mool net]

25 = 20 + 5

스물다섯
[seu mool da suht]

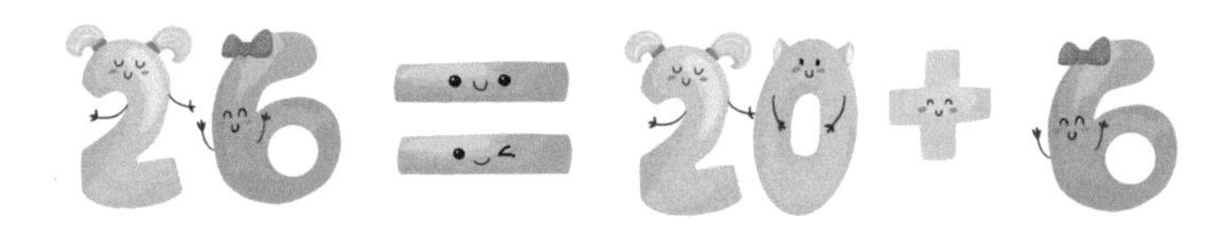

스물여섯
[seu mool yuh suht]

스물일곱
[seu mool il gop]

스물여덟
[seu mool yuh deol]

스물아홉
[seu mool ah hop]

서른
[suh reun]

Writing Numbers 21-30

Write the numbers next to each Korean word. The first one is the example.

[suh reun]	서른	30
[seu mool il gop]	스물일곱	
[seu mool yuh suht]	스물여섯	
[seu mool ah hop]	스물아홉	
[seu mool dool]	스물둘	
[seu mool da suht]	스물다섯	
[seu mool set]	스물셋	
[seu mool net]	스물넷	
[seu mool ha na]	스물하나	
[seu mool yuh deol]	스물여덟	

■ Choose the Korean words for numbers 11-20 from the word bank and write them next to their corresponding number.

21 ________________
[seu mool ha na]

26 ________________
[seu mool yuh suht]

22 ________________
[seu mool dool]

27 ________________
[seu mool il gop]

23 ________________
[seu mool set]

28 ________________
[seu mool yuh deol]

24 ________________
[seu mool net]

29 ________________
[seu mool ah hop]

25 ________________
[seu mool da suht]

30 ________________
[suh reun]

스물셋 서른 스물일곱 스물넷 스물다섯

스물아홉 스물여덟 스물하나 스물여섯 스물둘

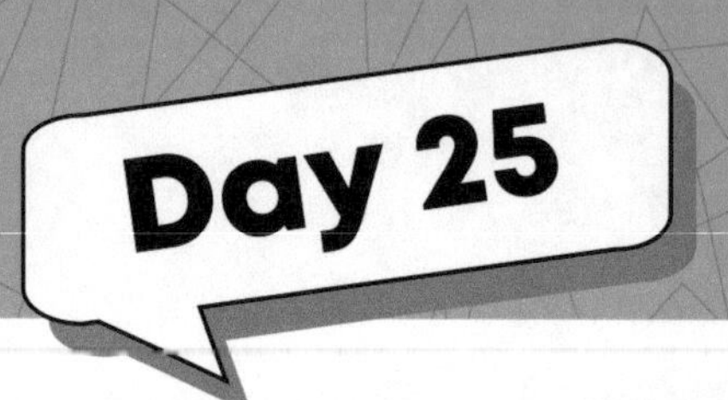

Date: / /

Reading Colors

Say each word out loud.

빨간색

[bbal gan saeg]

주황색

[joo hwang saeg]

초록색

[cho rok saeg]

보라색

[bo ra saeg]

갈색

[gal saeg]

하얀색

[ha yan saeg]

파란색

[pa ran saeg]

노란색

[no ran saeg]

■ Trace each color word below as you read out loud.

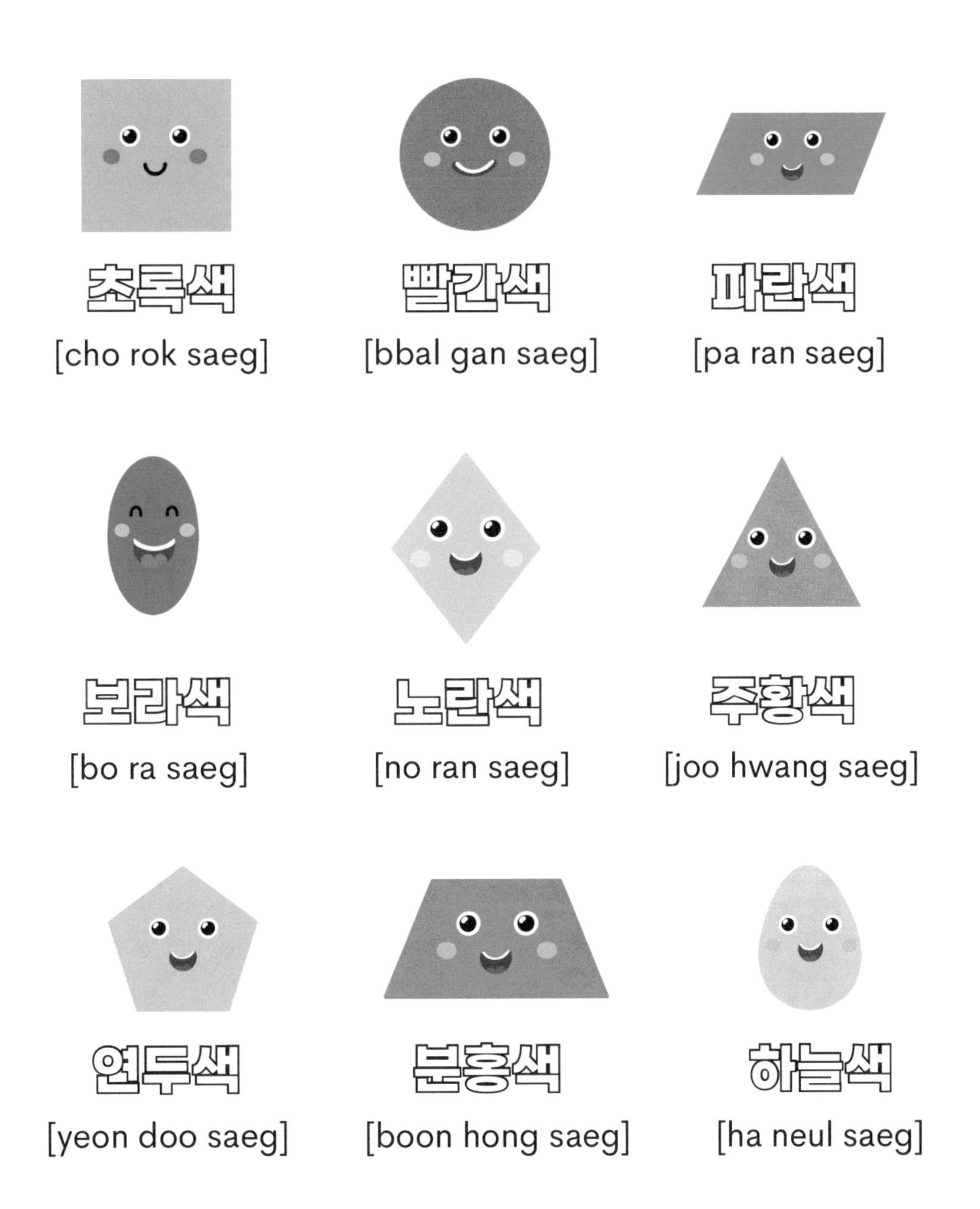

Matching Colors

보라색 ●	● [pa ran saeg]
초록색 ●	● [joo hwang saeg]
하얀색 ●	● [ha yan saeg]
분홍색 ●	● [yeon doo saeg]
하늘색 ●	● [bo ra saeg]
갈색 ●	● [no ran saeg]
주황색 ●	● [cho rok saeg]
빨간색 ●	● [ha neul saeg]
연두색 ●	● [boon hong saeg]
파란색 ●	● [gal saeg]
노란색 ●	● [bbal gan saeg]

Finding Colors

Circle the words from the word bank. You can find them in horizontal and vertical directions: → ← ↑ ↓ The first is the example.

초	늘	빨	라	두	록	간	라	얀	하
파	색	늘	하	하	색	두	록	보	보
색	황	주	갈	록	간	보	색	얀	하
간	색	주	하	늘	파	란	색	빨	홍
두	두	두	노	분	란	록	두	간	얀
보	연	홍	연	홍	연	주	초	색	주
노	란	색	초	색	빨	파	간	연	하
홍	두	란	록	연	간	두	란	보	연
색	색	갈	색	란	주	록	하	갈	록
황	황	갈	분	주	보	라	색	분	하

노란색 (Yellow)
주황색 (Orange)
하얀색 (White)
갈색 (Brown)
초록색 (Green)
연두색 (Light Green)
파란색 (Blue)
하늘색 (Sky Blue)
빨간색 (Red)
분홍색 (Pink)
보라색 (Purple)

Day 26

Date: / /

Tracing Colors

Trace the following words in the color of each word.

하얀색 하얀색 하얀색 하얀색 하얀색
[ha yan saeg]

노란색 노란색 노란색 노란색 노란색
[no ran saeg]

보라색 보라색 보라색 보라색 보라색
[bo ra saeg]

파란색 파란색 파란색 파란색 파란색
[pa ran saeg]

초록색 초록색 초록색 초록색 초록색
[cho rok saeg]

분홍색 분홍색 분홍색 분홍색 분홍색
[boon hong saeg]

연두색 연두색 연두색 연두색 연두색
[yeon doo saeg]

주황색 주황색 주황색 주황색 주황색
[joo hwang saeg]

하늘색 하늘색 하늘색 하늘색 하늘색
[ha neul saeg]

갈색 갈색 갈색 갈색 갈색
[gal saeg]

- Write the meaning of the Korean color words in English. Color the animal pictures using that color.

갈색 means

____

분홍색 means

____

빨간색 means

____

하얀색 means

____

노란색 means

____

초록색 means

____

파란색 means

____

주황색 means

____

보라색 means

____

Pink Brown Orange Yellow

Purple Red White Green Blue

■ Write the Korean color word for each clue word in the crossword puzzle.

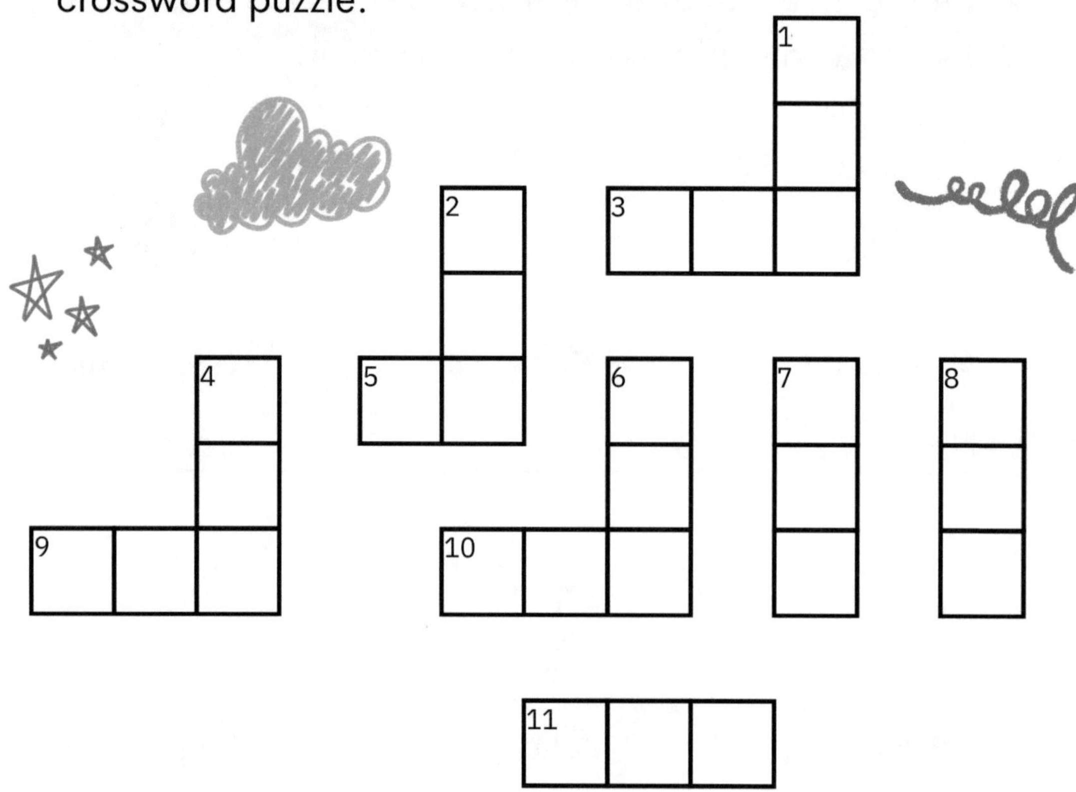

Across

3. Orange [joo hwang saeg]
5. Brown [gal saeg]
9. Red [bbal gan saeg]
10. Green [cho rok saeg]
11. White [ha yan saeg]

Down

1. Light Green [yeon doo saeg]
2. Sky Blue [ha neul saeg]
4. Purple [bo ra saeg]
6. Blue [pa ran saeg]
7. Yellow [no ran saeg]
8. Pink [boon hong saeg]

하얀색 빨간색 노란색 연두색 분홍색 파란색
초록색 하늘색 주황색 갈색 보라색

■ Color the flower according to the color words shown.

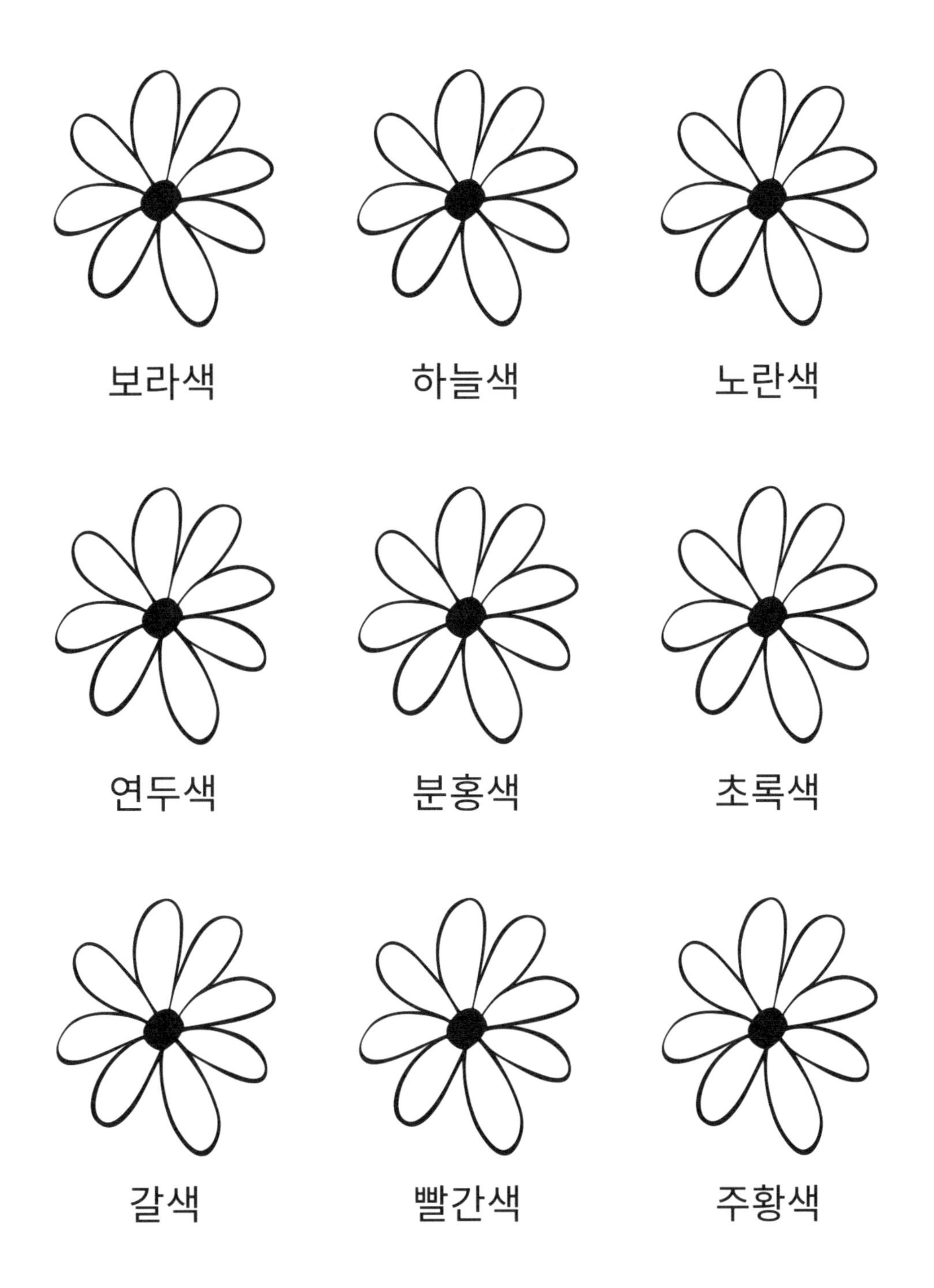

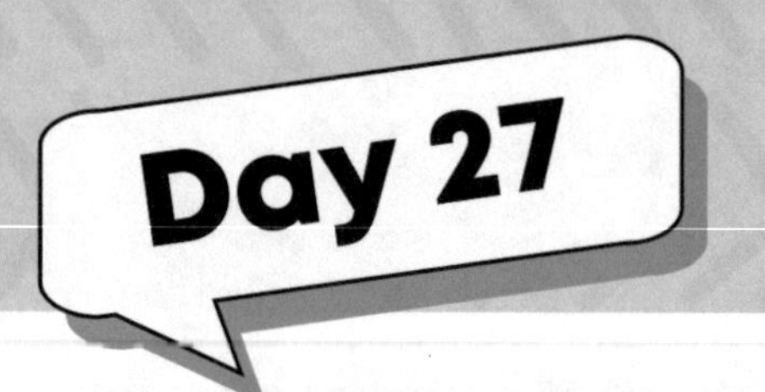

Date: / /

Tracing Face Words

Read and trace the words related to the face in Korean.

Face [uhl gul]

얼굴 얼굴 얼굴 얼굴

Eye [noon]

눈 눈 눈 눈

Ear [gwee]

귀 귀 귀 귀

Nose [ko]

코 코 코 코

Mouth [yip]

입 입 입 입

Teeth [yee]

이 이 이 이

Hair/ Head [muh lee]

머리 머리 머리 머리

Labeling the Face

Use the word bank to label each part of the face.

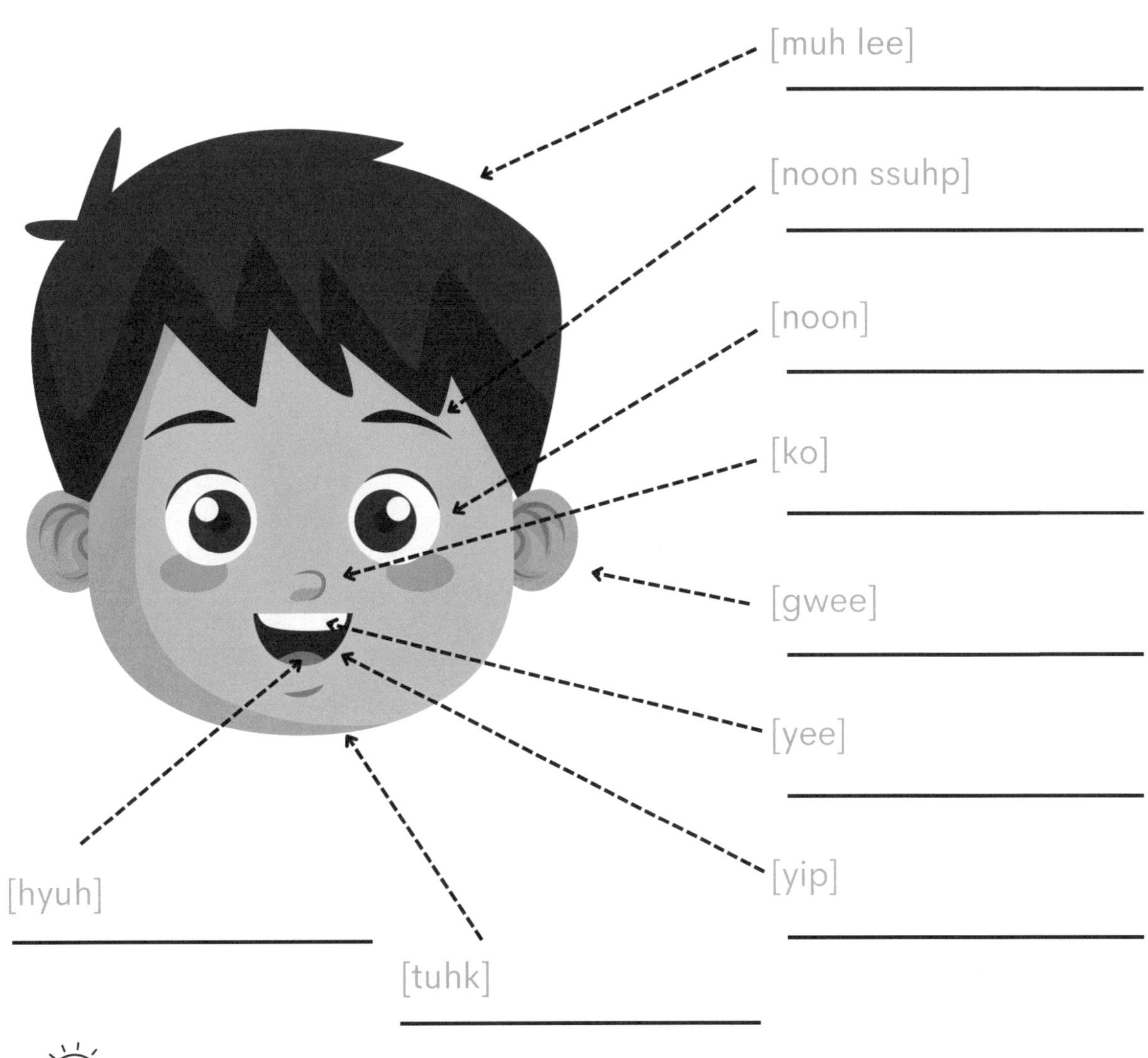

입 (Mouth) 이 (Teeth) 눈 (Eye) 귀 (Ear) 코 (Nose)
머리 (Hair/Head) 눈썹 (Eye brow) 턱 (Chin) 혀 (Tongue)

Labeling the Body

Use the word bank to label each part of the body.

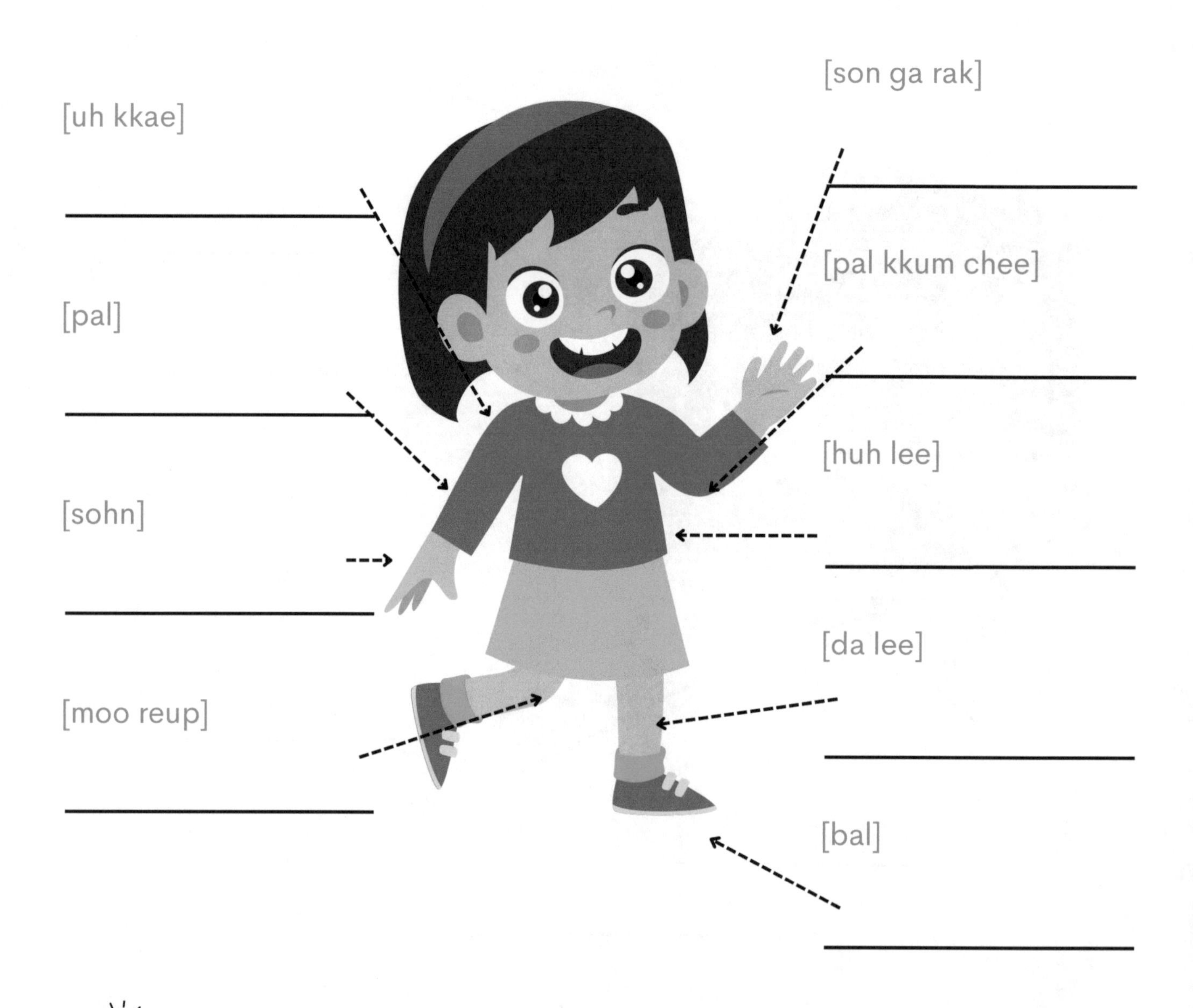

손 (Hand) 발 (Foot) 무릎 (Knee) 팔 (Arm) 다리 (Leg)
허리 (Waist) 어깨 (Shoulder) 손가락 (Finger) 팔꿈치 (Elbow)

■ Circle the words of body parts from the word bank. All of them are what we learned. You can find them in horizontal and vertical directions: → ← ↑ ↓

치	썹	썹	무	락	어	릎	릎	팔	치
꿈	눈	치	손	치	릎	꿈	무	팔	무
얼	꿈	얼	굴	무	발	눈	허	꿈	얼
리	어	얼	썹	무	가	리	눈	치	굴
허	어	깨	손	가	락	얼	릎	손	치
썹	손	릎	굴	썹	깨	깨	리	깨	치
깨	어	얼	썹	리	무	썹	머	무	가
가	깨	머	머	락	허	허	썹	얼	허
릎	치	발	락	가	발	눈	머	리	리
머	꿈	릎	얼	가	락	발	깨	리	발

팔꿈치 (Elbow) 손가락 (Finger) 눈썹 (Eye brow)

어깨 (Shoulder) 발가락 (Toe) 머리 (Hair/Head)

허리 (Waist) 무릎 (Knee) 얼굴 (Face)

Date: / /

Dad's Side Family

Read the Korean words out loud for family members on Dad's side, then trace each word.

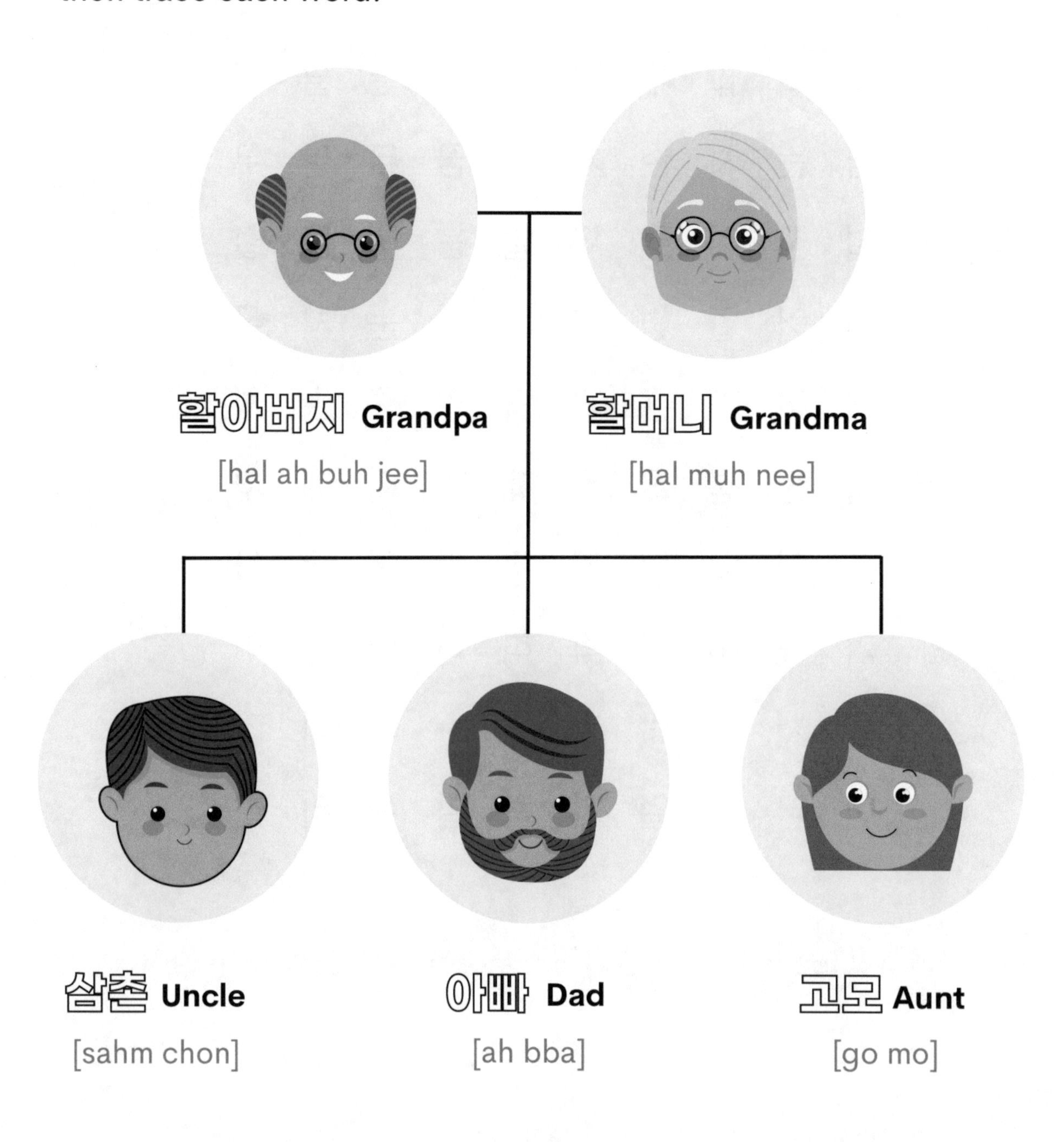

Mom's Side Family

Read the Korean words out loud for family members on Mom's side, then trace each word.

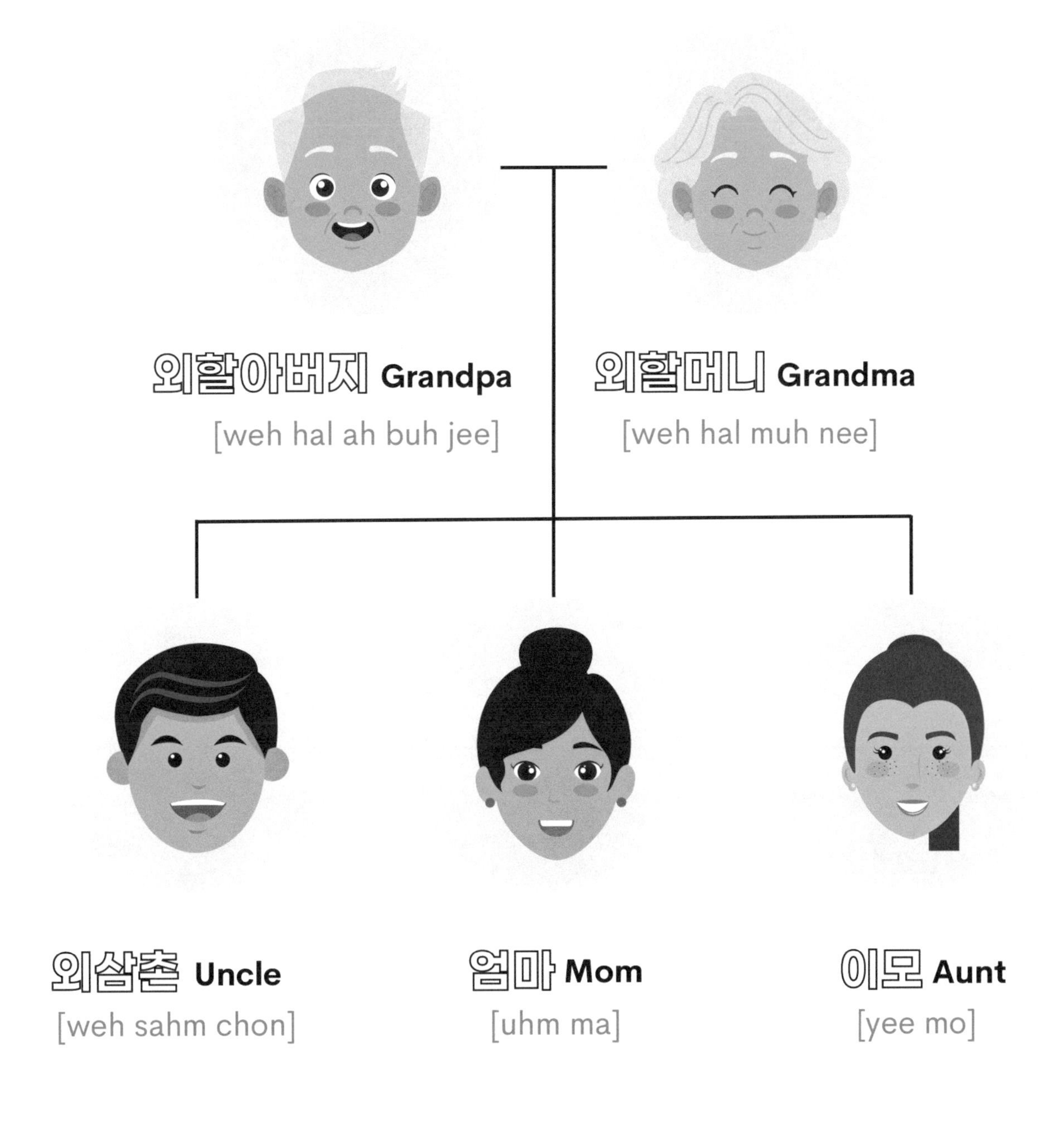

More Family Words

Read the Korean words for various family members out loud, then trace each word.

For males

Older sister

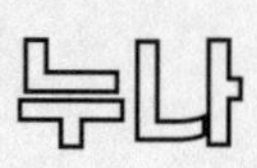

[noo na]

Older brother

[hyeong]

For females

Older sister

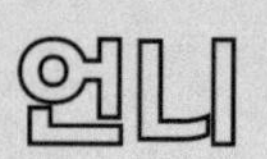

[uhn nee]

Older brother

[oh bba]

For everyone

Younger sibling

[dong saeng]

First cousins

[sa chon]

Family Tree

Place a photo or draw a picture of your family members in the circles, and write their titles in Korean. Use the word bank for help with the Korean titles if needed.

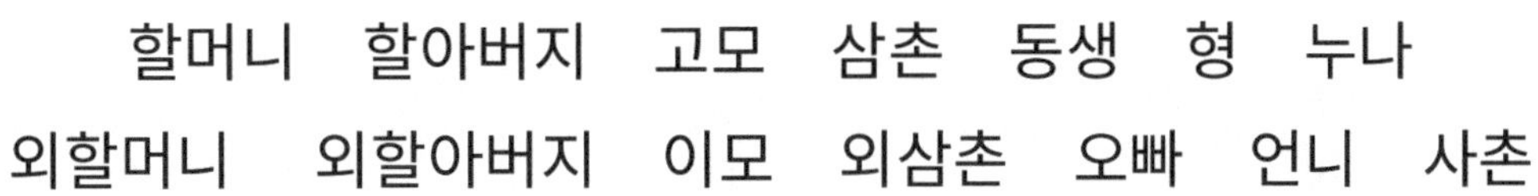

Day 29

Date: / /

Reading Months

Read each word out loud.

January

1월

[il wol]

February

2월

[yee wol]

March

3월

[sam wol]

April

4월

[sa wol]

May

5월

[oh wol]

June

6월

[yu wol]

July

7월

[chil wol]

August

8월

[pal wol]

September

9월

[goo wol]

October

10월

[shee wol]

November

11월

[ship il wol]

December

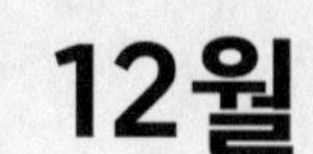

12월

[ship yee wol]

Wait, why do you read numbers differently?

In Korean, we have two ways to say numbers. One way uses Hangul, like '하나 [hana], 둘 [dool], 셋 [set]...', and the other uses numbers derived from Chinese characters, like '일 [il], 이 [yee], 삼 [sam]...'.

We use the latter system to count months and dates. Read the numbers below in both ways.

1	2	3	4	5
하나 [ha na]	둘 [dool]	셋 [set]	넷 [net]	다섯 [da suht]
일 [il]	이 [yee]	삼 [sam]	사 [sa]	오 [oh]

6	7	8	9	10
여섯 [yuh suht]	일곱 [il gop]	여덟 [yuh deol]	아홉 [ah hop]	열 [yeol]
육 [yuk]	칠 [chil]	팔 [pal]	구 [goo]	십 [ship]

Reading & Writing 11-20

Similar to the way of counting with '하나 [hana], 둘 [dul], 셋 [set]...', the numbers '일 [il], 이 [yee], 삼 [sam]...' follow the same pattern after 십 [ship].

You continue with '십일 [ship il]' for 11, '십이 [ship yee]' for 12, '십삼 [ship sam]' for 13, and so on. Write the pronunciation next to each number.

11 ____________ [ship il]

12 ____________ [ship yee]

13 ____________ [ship sam]

14 ____________ [ship sa]

15 ____________ [ship oh]

16 ____________ [ship yook]

17 ____________ [ship chil]

18 ____________ [ship pal]

19 ____________ [ship goo]

20 ____________ [yee ship]

십일 십오 십구 십육 십삼

십사 십팔 이십 □십이 십칠

Write Months

Choose the Korean words for months from the box below and write them next to their correct phonetic pronunciations.

shee wol	chil wol
sa wol	il wol
yee wol	goo wol
pal wol	ship yee wol
sam wol	yu wol
oh wol	ship il wol

1월 2월 3월 4월 5월 6월
7월 8월 9월 10월 11월 12월

Why do 'June' and 'October' sound different?

'6월' is more like **[yu wol]** than [yuk wol], and '10월' is said as **[shee wol]**, not [ship wol]. It's because the original ways were hard to say, so the pronunciation naturally changed to be easier.

Matching Months

January •	• 삼월 [sam wol]
February •	• 유월 [yu wol]
March •	• 팔월 [pal wol]
April •	• 칠월 [chil wol]
May •	• 구월 [goo wol]
June •	• 십이월 [ship yee wol]
July •	• 시월 [shee wol]
August •	• 일월 [il wol]
September •	• 사월 [sa wol]
October •	• 오월 [oh wol]
November •	• 십일월 [ship il wol]
December •	• 이월 [yee wol]

Day 30

Date: / /

Reading Dates

Similar to months, for counting days, use '일 (il), 이 (yee), 삼 (sam)'. Read the dates listed on the left side out loud, then write the correct dates for the questions on the right side. The first one is the example.

1일 [il il]

2일 [yee il]

3일 [sam il]

4일 [sa il]

5일 [oh il]

6일 [yuk il]

7일 [chil il]

8일 [pal il]

9일 [goo il]

10일 [ship il]

20일 [yee ship il]

30일 [sam ship il]

- [ship chil il] is: 17일
- [ship oh il] is: ____________
- [ship yuk il] is: ____________
- [yee ship chil il] is: ____________
- [yee ship yee il] is: ____________
- [sam ship il il] is: ____________
- [ship sam il] is: ____________

Matching Dates

Match the dates in Korean to their pronunciations.

[ship yuk il] ●	● 23일
[sam ship il] ●	● 16일
[ship chil il] ●	● 9일
[goo il] ●	● 14일
[ship sa il] ●	● 28일
[yee ship yee il] ●	● 11일
[yee ship pal il] ●	● 26일
[yee ship sam il] ●	● 17일
[ship il il] ●	● 22일
[yee ship yuk il] ●	● 30일

Writing Days

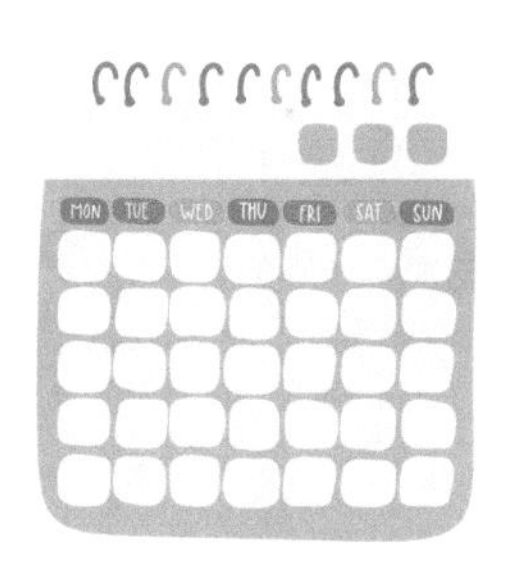

Write the Korean words for the days of the week. The first is the example.

Korean	English	Practice
월요일 [wol yo il]	Monday	월요일 월요일 월요일
화요일 [hwa yo il]	Tuesday	
수요일 [soo yo il]	Wednesday	
목요일 [mok yo il]	Thursday	
금요일 [geum yo il]	Friday	
토요일 [to yo il]	Saturday	
일요일 [il yo il]	Sunday	

■ Write the Korean word for each clue word in the crossword puzzle.

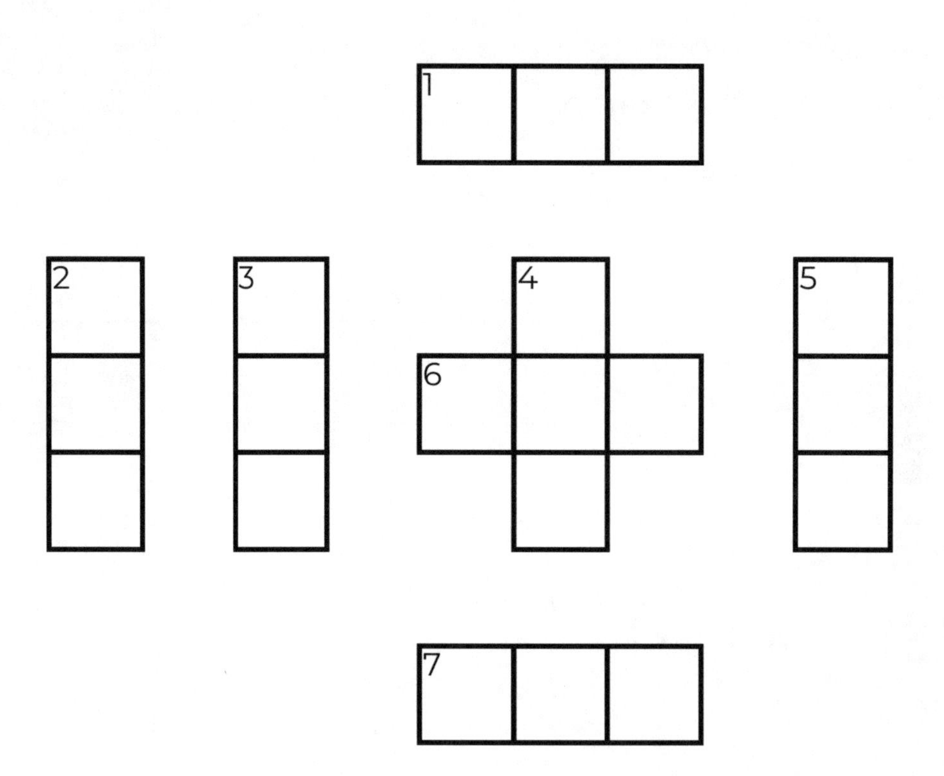

Across

1. Friday [geum yo il]
6. Wednesday [soo yo il]
7. Sunday [il yo il]

Down

2. Tuesday [hwa yo il]
3. Monday [wol yo il]
4. Thursday [mok yo il]
5. Saturday [to yo il]

월요일 화요일 수요일 목요일 금요일 토요일 일요일

Answer Key

Page 6

나무 사자 아빠

가방 다리 기차

Page 7

약 야구 양말

이야기 양 약국

Page 8

엄마 거미 선물

두더지 이어폰 어린이

Page 9

여우 영어 겨울

셔틀버스 여자 여섯

Page 10

오이 모자 고양이

토끼 손 고기

Page 11

요리 요거트 교실

요트 용 욕조

Page 12

우산 수박 비누

축구 호두 구두

Page 13

우유 튜브 세균

휴지 자유 귤

Page 14

그네 버스 브로콜리

사슴 그림자 스펀지

Page 15

피자 치약 머리띠

딸기 비행기 시소

Page 16

uh	ㅓ	woo	ㅜ
yo	ㅛ	ah	ㅏ
eu	ㅡ	yah	ㅑ
yuh	ㅕ	yee	ㅣ
oh	ㅗ	yu	ㅠ

Page 17

ㅜ	**woo**	ㅡ	**eu**
ㅑ	**ya**	ㅕ	**yuh**
ㅗ	**oh**	ㅏ	**ah**
ㅣ	**yee**	ㅛ	**yo**
ㅠ	**yu**	ㅓ	**uh**

Page 19

기차

고기

가방

냉장고

햄버거

이야기

Page 21

바나나

피아노

나쵸

너구리

도넛

눈사람

Page 23

다리

샐러드

두부

바다

사다리

다리미

Page 25

콜라

코끼리

리모컨

로보트

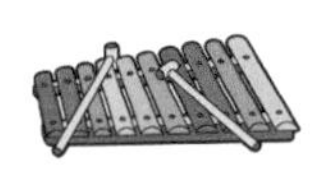
실로폰

라면

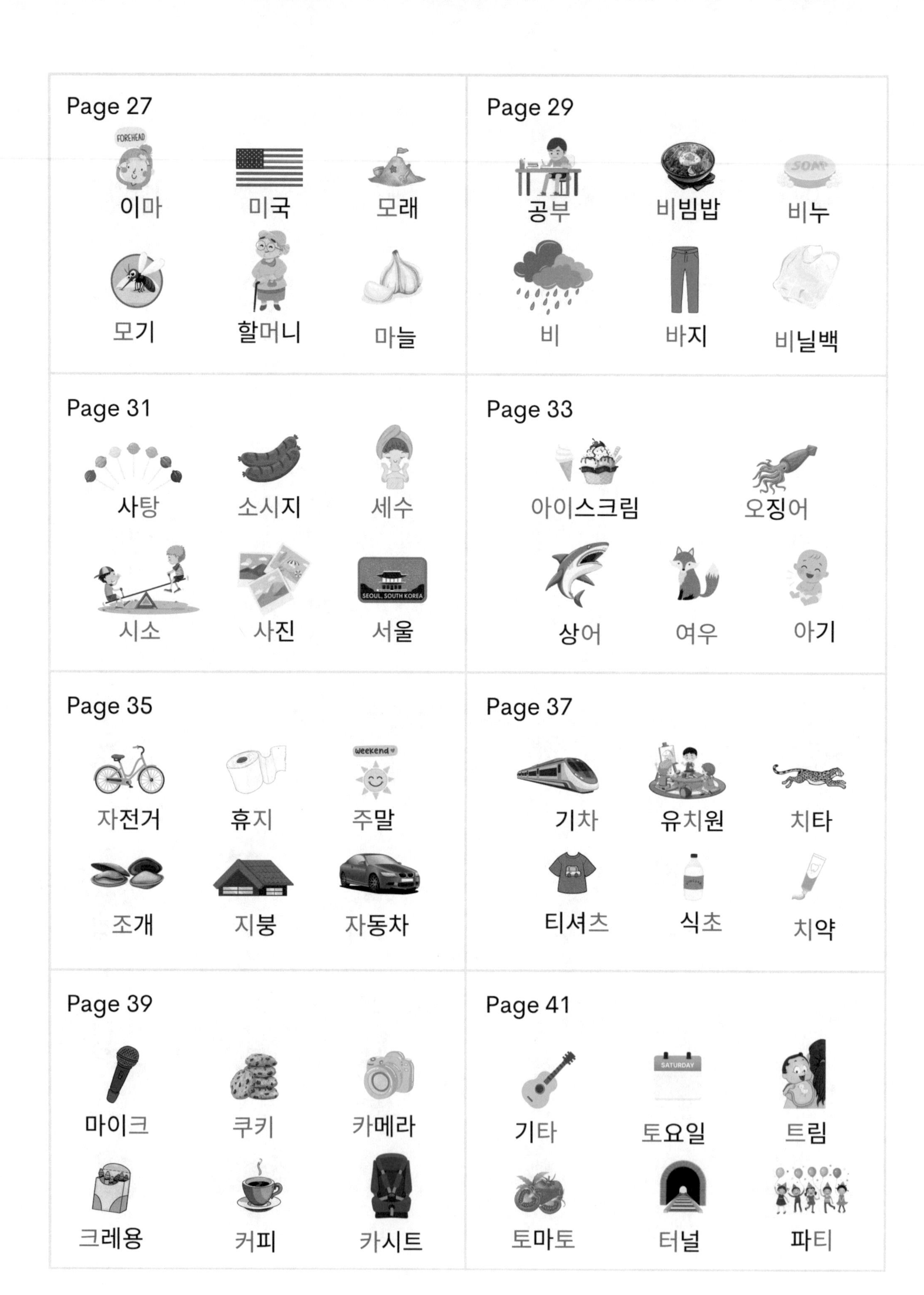

Page 27
FOREHEAD
이마
미국
모래
모기
할머니
마늘
Page 29
공부
비빔밥
비누
비
바지
비닐백
Page 31
사탕
소시지
세수
시소
사진
SEOUL, SOUTH KOREA
서울
Page 33
아이스크림
오징어
상어
여우
아기
Page 35
자전거
휴지
weekend
주말
조개
지붕
자동차
Page 37
기차
유치원
치타
티셔츠
식초
치약
Page 39
마이크
쿠키
카메라
크레용
커피
카시트
Page 41
기타
SATURDAY
토요일
트림
토마토
터널
파티

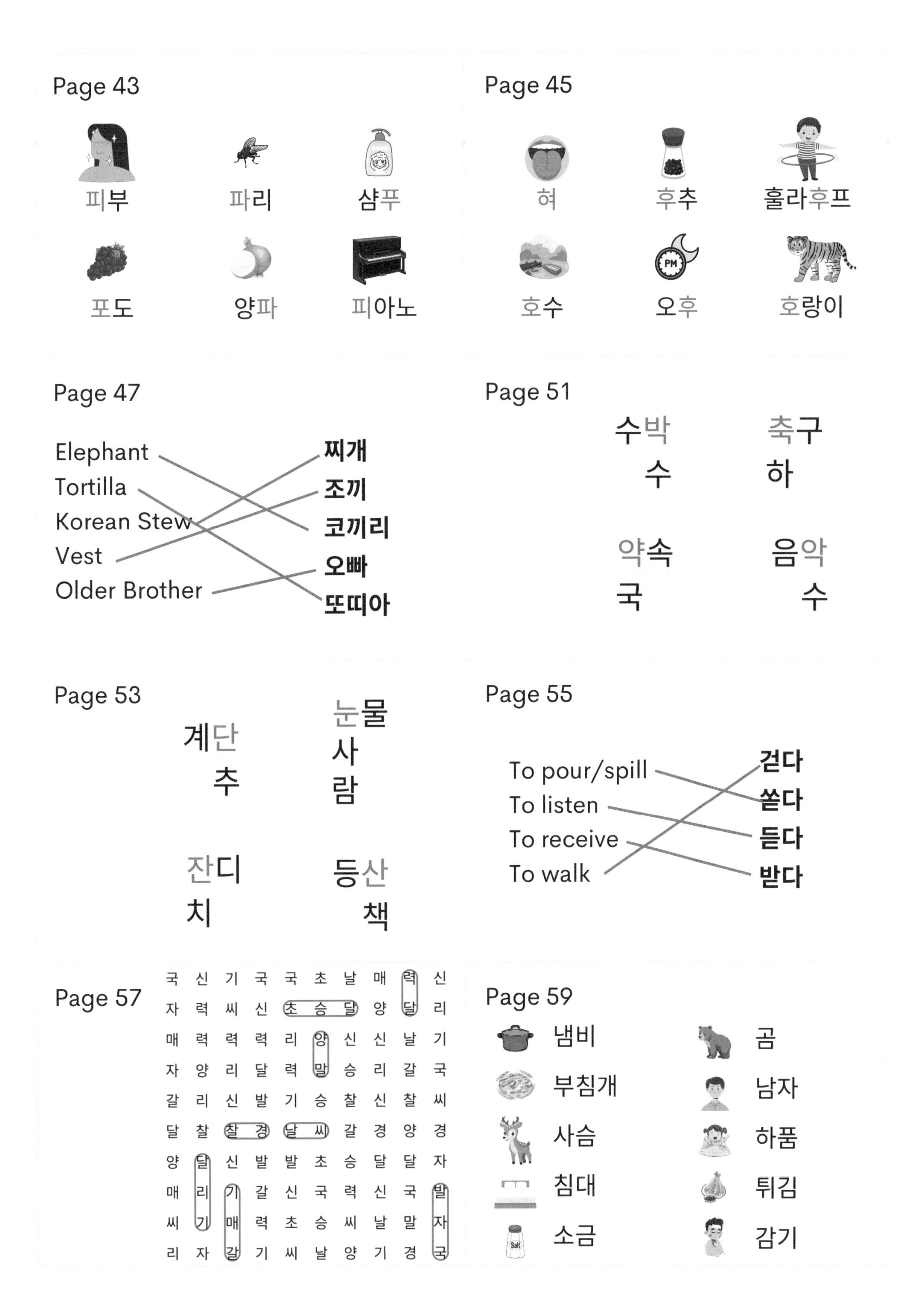
Page 43
피부
파리
샴푸
포도
양파
피아노
Page 45
혀
후추
훌라후프
호수
오후
호랑이
Page 47
Elephant
Tortilla
Korean Stew
Vest
Older Brother
찌개
조끼
코끼리
오빠
또띠아
Page 51
수박
수
축구
하
약속
국
음악
수
Page 53
계단
추
눈물
사
람
잔디
치
등산
책
Page 55
To pour/spill
To listen
To receive
To walk
걷다
쏟다
듣다
받다
Page 57
국 신 기 국 국 초 날 매 력 신
자 력 씨 신 초 승 달 양 달 리
매 력 력 력 리 양 신 신 날 기
자 양 리 달 력 말 승 리 갈 국
갈 리 신 발 기 승 찰 신 찰 씨
달 찰 찰 경 달 씨 갈 경 양 경
양 달 신 발 발 초 승 달 달 자
매 리 기 갈 신 국 력 신 국 발
씨 기 매 력 초 승 씨 날 말 자
리 자 감 기 씨 날 양 기 경 국
Page 59
냄비
부침개
사슴
침대
소금
곰
남자
하품
튀김
감기

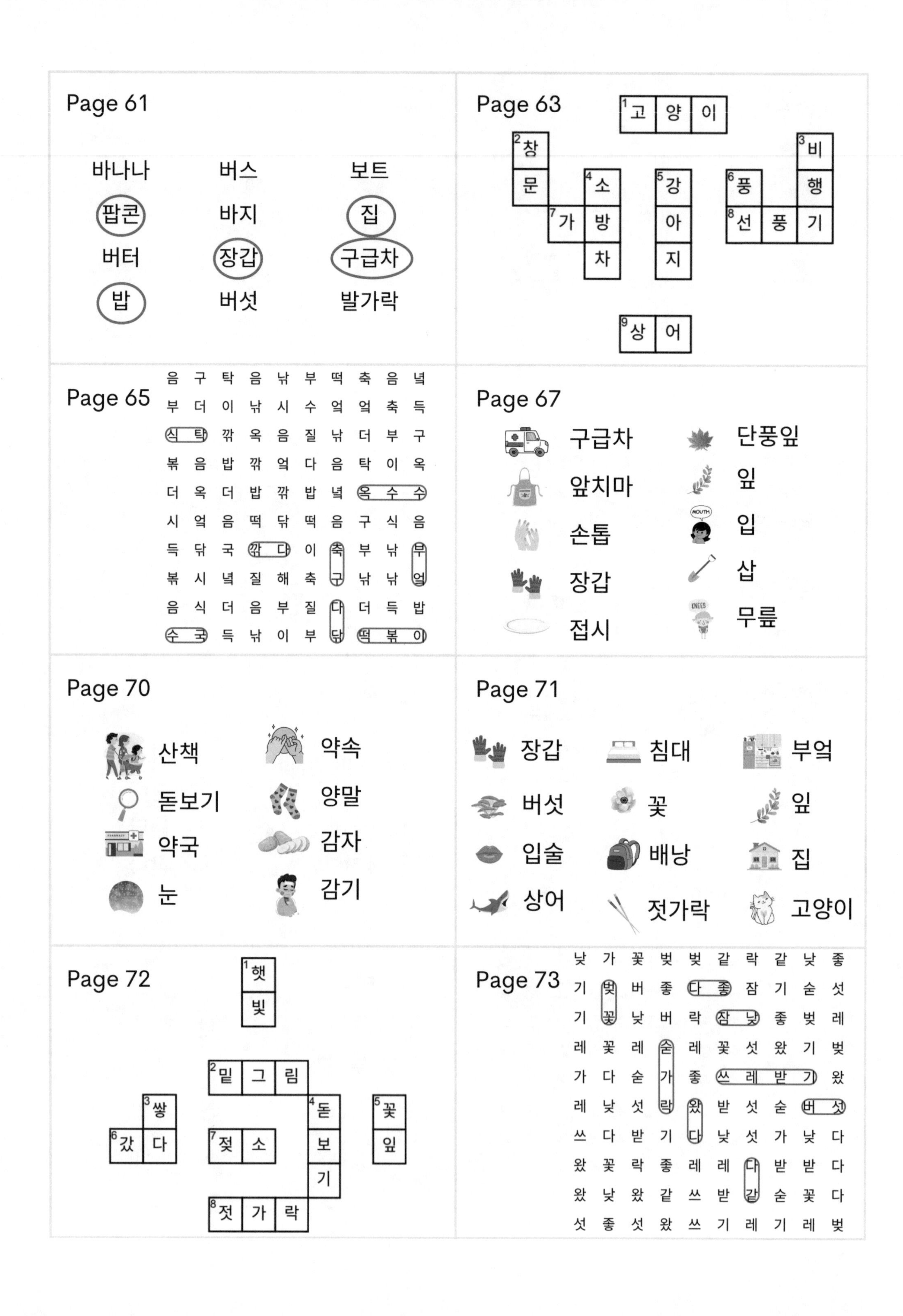

Page 61
바나나 버스 보트
팝콘 바지 집
버터 장갑 구급차
밥 버섯 발가락
Page 63
1 고 양 이
2 창 문
3 비 행 기
4 소 방 차
5 강 아 지
6 풍
7 가 방
8 선 풍 기
9 상 어
Page 65
음 구 탁 음 낚 부 떡 축 음 녘
부 더 이 낚 시 수 엌 엌 축 득
식 탁 깎 옥 음 질 낚 더 부 구
볶 음 밥 깎 엌 다 음 탁 이 옥
더 옥 더 밥 깎 밥 녘 옥 수 수
시 엌 음 떡 닭 떡 음 구 식 음
득 닭 국 깎 다 이 축 부 낚 부
볶 시 녘 질 해 축 구 낚 낚 엌
음 식 더 음 부 질 다 더 득 밥
수 국 득 낚 이 부 닭 떡 볶 이
Page 67
구급차 단풍잎
앞치마 잎
손톱 입
장갑 삽
접시 무릎
MOUTH
KNEES
Page 70
산책 약속
돋보기 양말
약국 감자
눈 감기
Page 71
장갑 침대 부엌
버섯 꽃 잎
입술 배낭 집
상어 젓가락 고양이
Page 72
1 햇 빛
2 밑 그 림
3 쌓 다
4 돋 보 기
5 꽃 잎
6 갔 다
7 젖 소
8 젓 가 락
Page 73
낮 가 꽃 벚 벚 같 락 같 낮 좋
기 벚 버 좋 다 좋 잠 기 숟 섯
기 꽃 낮 버 락 잠 낮 좋 벚 레
레 꽃 레 숟 레 꽃 섯 왔 기 벚
가 다 숟 가 좋 쓰 레 받 기 왔
레 낮 섯 락 왔 받 섯 숟 버 섯
쓰 다 받 기 다 낮 섯 가 낮 다
왔 꽃 락 좋 레 레 다 받 받 다
왔 낮 왔 같 쓰 받 같 숟 꽃 다
섯 좋 섯 왔 쓰 기 레 기 레 벚

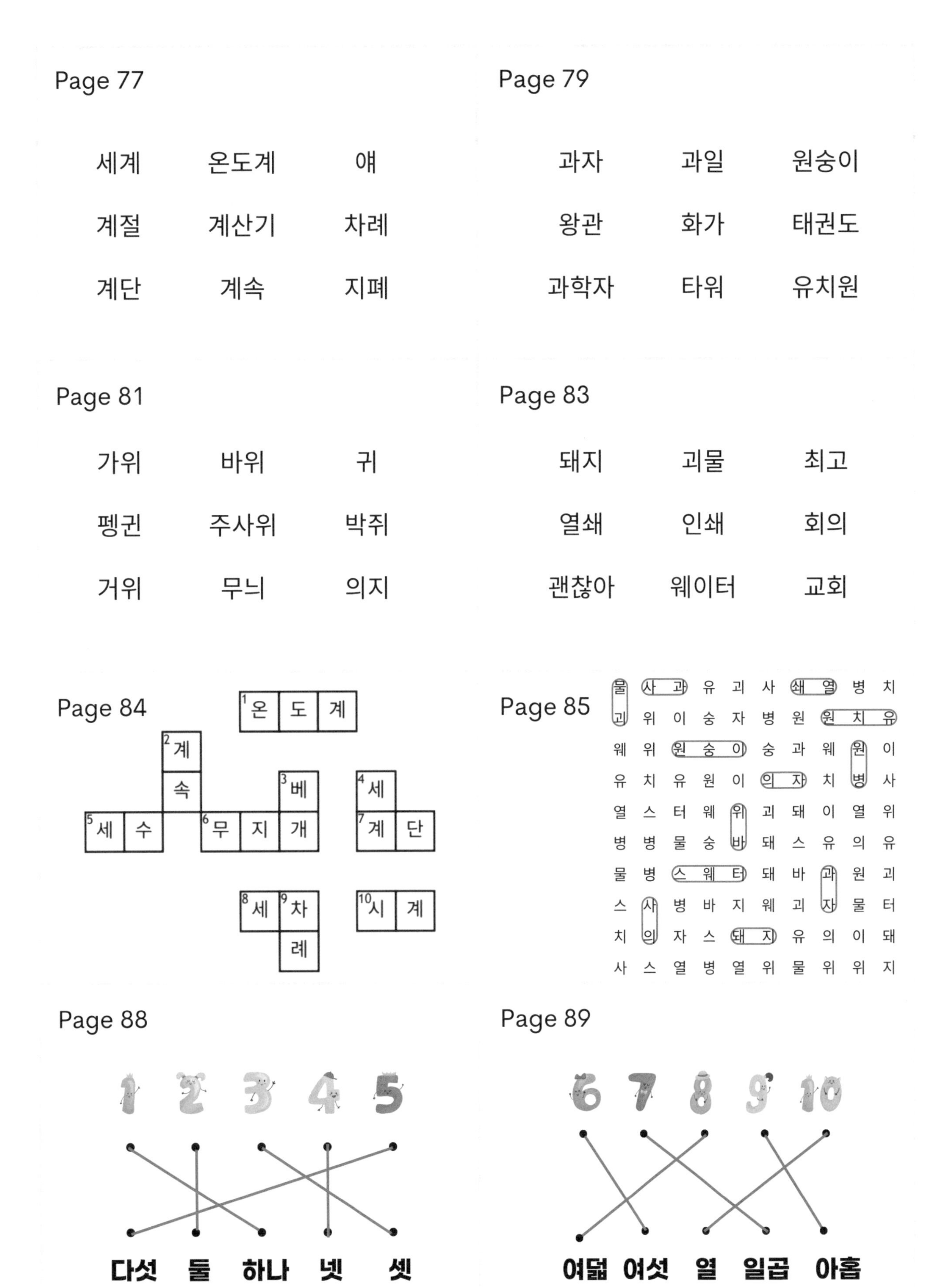

Page 77
세계 온도계 얘
계절 계산기 차례
계단 계속 지폐
Page 79
과자 과일 원숭이
왕관 화가 태권도
과학자 타워 유치원
Page 81
가위 바위 귀
펭귄 주사위 박쥐
거위 무늬 의지
Page 83
돼지 괴물 최고
열쇠 인쇄 회의
괜찮아 웨이터 교회
Page 84
1 온 도 계
2 계 속
3 베 개
4 세 7 계 단
5 세 수
6 무 지 개
8 세 9 차 례
10 시 계
Page 85
물 사 과 유 괴 사 쇄 열 병 치
괴 위 이 숭 자 병 원 원 치 유
웨 위 원 숭 이 숭 과 웨 원 이
유 치 유 원 이 의 자 치 병 사
열 스 터 웨 위 괴 돼 이 열 위
병 병 물 숭 바 돼 스 유 의 유
물 병 스 웨 터 돼 바 과 원 괴
스 사 병 바 지 웨 괴 자 물 터
치 의 자 스 돼 지 유 의 이 돼
사 스 열 병 열 위 물 위 위 지
Page 88
1 2 3 4 5
다섯 둘 하나 넷 셋
Page 89
6 7 8 9 10
여덟 여섯 열 일곱 아홉

Page 90-91

3 셋	8 여덟
4 넷	6 여섯
1 하나	5 다섯
2 둘	10 열
	9 아홉
	7 일곱

Page 92

1 하나	6 여섯
2 둘	7 일곱
3 셋	8 여덟
4 넷	9 아홉
5 다섯	10 열

Page 93

넷 4	여덟 8
일곱 7	열 10
셋 3	여섯 6
다섯 5	둘 2
하나 1	아홉 9

Page 96

12 열둘	16 열여섯
15 열다섯	14 열넷
13 열셋	17 열입곱
18 열여덟	19 열아홉
20 스물	11 열하나

Page 97

11 열하나	16 열여섯
12 열둘	17 열입곱
13 열셋	18 열여덟
14 열넷	19 열아홉
15 열다섯	20 스물

Page 100

서른 30	스물다섯 25
스물일곱 27	스물셋 23
스물여섯 26	스물넷 24
스물아홉 29	스물하나 21
스물둘 22	스물여덟 28

Page 101

21 스물하나	26 스물여섯
22 스물둘	27 스물일곱
23 스물셋	28 스물여덟
24 스물넷	29 스물아홉
25 스물다섯	30 서른

Page 104

보라색	갈색
초록색	주황색
하얀색	빨간색
분홍색	연두색
하늘색	파란색
	노란색

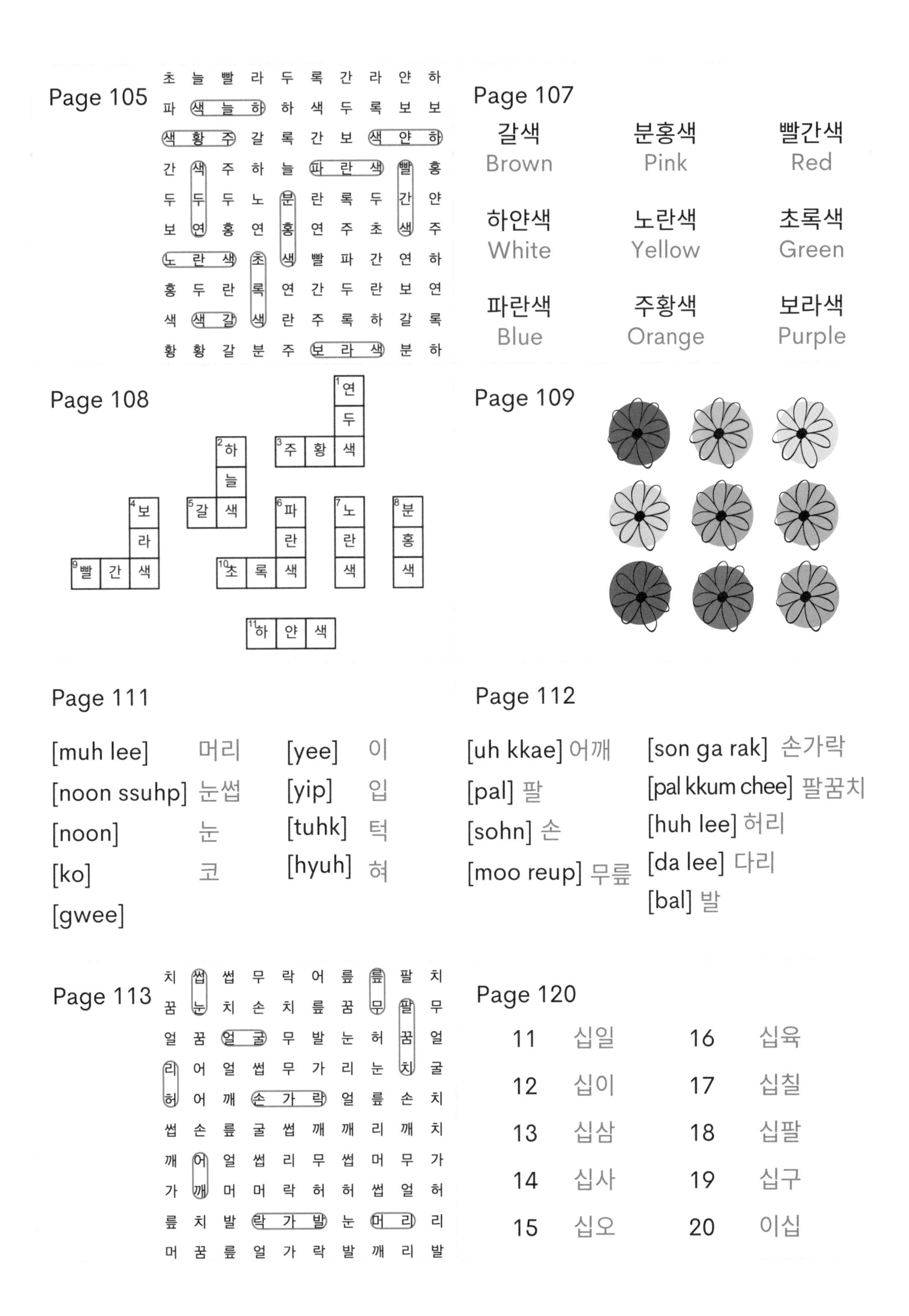
Page 105
초 늘 빨 라 두 록 간 라 얀 하
파 색 늘 하 하 색 두 록 보 보
색 황 주 갈 록 간 보 색 얀 하
간 색 주 하 늘 파 란 색 빨 홍
두 두 두 노 분 란 록 두 간 얀
보 연 홍 연 홍 연 주 초 색 주
노 란 색 초 색 빨 파 간 연 하
홍 두 란 록 연 간 두 란 보 연
색 색 갈 색 란 주 록 하 갈 록
황 황 갈 분 주 보 라 색 분 하
Page 107
갈색
Brown
분홍색
Pink
빨간색
Red
하얀색
White
노란색
Yellow
초록색
Green
파란색
Blue
주황색
Orange
보라색
Purple
Page 108
1 연 두 색
2 하 늘 색
3 주 황 색
4 보 라 색
5 갈 색
6 파 란 색
7 노 란 색
8 분 홍 색
9 빨 간 색
10 초 록 색
11 하 얀 색
Page 109
Page 111
[muh lee] 머리
[noon ssuhp] 눈썹
[noon] 눈
[ko] 코
[gwee]
[yee] 이
[yip] 입
[tuhk] 턱
[hyuh] 혀
Page 112
[uh kkae] 어깨
[pal] 팔
[sohn] 손
[moo reup] 무릎
[son ga rak] 손가락
[pal kkum chee] 팔꿈치
[huh lee] 허리
[da lee] 다리
[bal] 발
Page 113
치 썹 썹 무 락 어 릎 릎 팔 치
꿈 눈 치 손 치 릎 꿈 무 팔 무
얼 꿈 얼 굴 무 발 눈 허 꿈 얼
리 어 얼 썹 무 가 리 눈 치 굴
허 어 깨 손 가 락 얼 릎 손 치
썹 손 릎 굴 썹 깨 깨 리 깨 치
깨 어 얼 썹 리 무 썹 머 무 가
가 깨 머 머 락 허 허 썹 얼 허
릎 치 발 락 가 발 눈 머 리 리
머 꿈 릎 얼 가 락 발 깨 리 발
Page 120
11 십일
12 십이
13 십삼
14 십사
15 십오
16 십육
17 십칠
18 십팔
19 십구
20 이십

Page 121

shee wol	10월	chil wol	7월
sa wol	4월	il wol	1월
yee wol	2월	goo wol	9월
pal wol	8월	ship yee wol	12월
sam wol	3월	yu wol	6월
oh wol	5월	ship il wol	11월

Page 122

January	일월	July	칠월
February	이월	August	팔월
March	삼월	September	구월
April	사월	October	시월
May	오월	November	십일월
June	유월	December	십이월

Page 123

[ship oh il]	15일
[ship yuk il]	16일
[yee ship chil il]	27일
[yee ship yee il]	22일
[sam ship il il]	30일
[ship sam il]	13일

Page 124

[ship yuk il]	16일	[yee ship yee il]	22일
[sam ship il]	30일	[yee ship pal il]	28일
[ship chil il]	17일	[yee ship sam il]	23일
[goo il]	9일	[ship il il]	11일
[ship sa il]	14일	[yee ship yuk il]	26일

Page 126

		1 금	요	일	
2 화	3 월		4 목		5 토
요	요	6 수	요	일	요
일	일		일		일
		7 일	요	일	

Explore More Korean-English Learning Adventures!

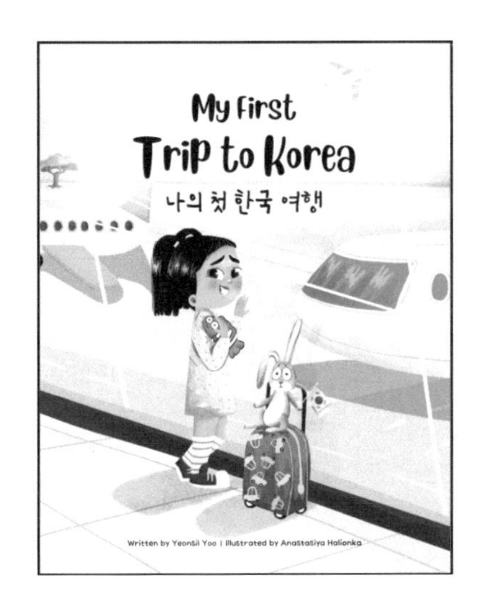

Bilingual
Korean-English
Picture Book

Ages 4-7

Bilingual
Korean-English
Picture Book

Ages 5-8

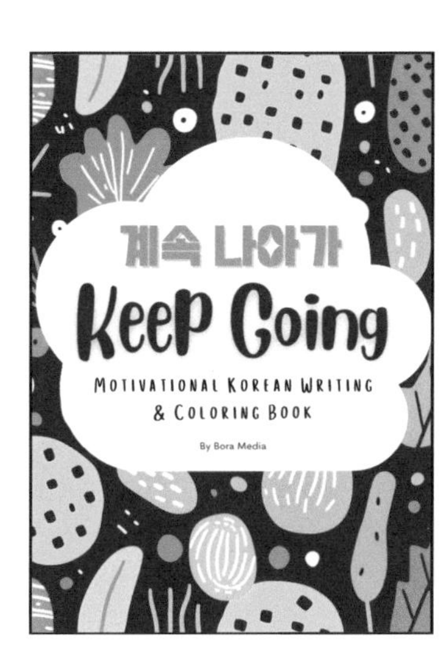

Motivational
Korean Writing &
Coloring Book

All Ages

Made in United States
Troutdale, OR
03/24/2024